Lazy Pe
to Emotional Healing

For Amy

Keep up your great work

with very best wishes

Andrew

November 2004

Lazy Person's Guide to Emotional Healing

Using Flower Essences Successfully

Dr Andrew Tresidder

Newleaf

Newleaf

an imprint of
Gill & Macmillan Ltd
Hume Avenue, Park West
Dublin 12
with associated companies throughout the world
www.gillmacmillan.ie

Print origination by Vermillion
Printed by ColourBooks Ltd, Dublin

A catalogue record is available for this book from the British Library.

1 3 5 4 2

Trillium Grandiflorum
(Wake-Robin)

To my wife Hilary,
for all her loving support and encouragement.

And to all those who have given me
so much inspiration and help.

Please take a moment of silence for yourself.
Just for a moment, look into your heart of hearts.
What sort of person would you really like to be?
What qualities would you like?
What does it feel like?
Spend a few moments experiencing this.
Enjoy the warm glow you feel.
You have just touched part of your
true inner nature – your real self.
Remember this vision as you return back to
the present. This book is dedicated to you,
and to the vision that you have just touched.
To the shining souls that we all are if we did but realise it.
Here are some of the tools to help you remember who you are.
To the God force which is at the core of all things.
To the Christ within you.

Viola 'Roggli Giants'

Namaskrama. I salute the divinity within you.

Dear Lord and Father of mankind,
Forgive our foolish ways!
Reclothe us in our rightful mind,
In purer lives thy service find,
In deeper reverence praise.

Drop thy still dews of quietness,
Till all our strivings cease;
Take from our souls the strain and stress,
And let our ordered lives confess
The beauty of thy peace.

J.G. Whittier

Contents

NB: *Some of the material in this book is so important I have repeated it twice.*

Disclaimer

All information in this book is given in good faith. However, flower essences do not work all the time for everybody, nor are they a complete or exclusive system of healing for the emotions. This book is not intended to deliver any universal panacea, but is a synthesis of experiences designed to be a map to help others on a journey toward greater health.

This book is for reference only and should not be used instead of properly qualified medical or health practitioner advice. Please always get an orthodox medical diagnosis, particularly to exclude unsuspected and undiagnosed illness, and as part of your partnership on your journey of health.

It is hoped that the information shared in this book will help many thousands of people to help themselves to achieve greater health. However, it is not possible for either the author or the publisher to guarantee health for the reader – we all have to tread our own unique and sacred journey in life. Therefore the author and the publisher cannot accept responsibility for the reader of this book or the user of any essences or techniques described in this book.

Important Note

Dr Bach advised that flower essences should not be used in cases of psychosis, schizophrenia, possession and such. This advice is still valid today, as the underlying pathology is not just a simple psychological imbalance.

If you are allergic to alcohol or to any particular flower, do not take essences by mouth.

Flower essences are not intended to be used instead of medical advice or treatment. Please observe this for your own protection, and seek medical advice from a qualified practitioner.

The author has made efforts to trace all relevant copyright owners. If anyone has unfortunately not been traced, the author offers his apologies and would like to make full acknowledgment in reprints where possible.

Preface

Being a botanist, son of a pharmacist and someone who knows
something about the power of plants in the process of healing,
I read this book with great interest. It is an excellent review of the
multitude of flower essences now on sale in many retail outlets.
Essences are selling like hot cakes, so much so, that it is trite
to say that tens of thousands of satisfied customers can't be wrong.

It is also a review by a practising General Practitioner who was trained
in one of the world's great schools of orthodox medicine as recently
as 1983. What is more, he works in the National Health Service and
trains others in the practice of flower essence therapy. So it is very
refreshing to hear about all his research on and faith in *materia medica*
that has been in use for over 60,000 years in what some would call
unorthodox ways.

My main grumble about the book is that I, like Friedrich
Hahnemann, father of homeopathy, believe that the relationship
between the healer and those being healed is of key importance
in the process of healing. However, as not all medical doctors are as
enlightened as the author, perhaps this book is a way in which sceptics
can begin to take those first steps towards the process of emotional
healing. Accept. Acknowledge. Forgive. If reading this book does no
more than this it will be a great step in the right direction. However,
my advice would always be to go to a fully qualified practitioner
and work with them to that end, for then and only then can you
complete the healing process by saying 'thank you' to the healer who
helped you on the way. Say it with flowers!

David Bellamy

Bedburn, December 1999

Acknowledgments

This book would not have been possible without the tremendous
support of many people. Firstly Hilary, Frances, Isabel and Rose.
Secondly, those who encouraged me to write, including my publisher,
Michael Gill, Alick Bartholomew, Palden Jenkins, all the team at
Gill & Macmillan and my agent Susan Mears. Thanks also to Clare
Harvey, Glenn and Nancy Broughton and Caro Ness. Next my
partners, staff and colleagues in General Practice in Chard, Somerset,
especially Dr Peter Glanvill and Dr Will Harris. Most importantly all
those people – including my patients and my family – who have
permitted me to use flower essences and many other healing
techniques as well as the orthodox medicine they were expecting.
From you particularly I have learned so much that has helped to bring
about this book.

Neither would this work have been possible without the superb
support, encouragement and help given to me personally and in the
work they have done, by so many friends in the Flower Essence
Community. Thank you all! You know who you are!

Finally to my mother, father and Tony, my brothers, their families,
Nanna and all my other friends and relations – for being there when I
needed you and for all the love and help on the journey of life.

Illustrations

Grateful thanks to Jannet Unite, Vivien Williamson and Peter
Glanvill for their photographs, to Jethro Crabb and Greg Smith for
the drawings and to Geoff King for the cover photograph.

Poem

The hymn 'Dear Lord and Father of Mankind' by J.G. Whittier is
reproduced from *Hymns Ancient & Modern*, Revised Edition (1950),
by kind permission of the publishers, SCM-Canterbury Press Ltd.

Emotional Healing with Flower Essences –

A Lazy Person's Guide

Zephyranthes
Grandiflora

Science now recognises what many people know intuitively, that how we feel has a major impact on our physical well-being. In other words, emotional well-being goes hand in hand with physical health.

Given a handful of broken glass everybody knows what to do. To be given a heartful of broken emotions however throws many of us into confusion. Rather than drop or process them people hide, deny, bury or secrete the wounds within themselves. Most of us carry lots of emotional broken glass within us consciously and unconsciously, painfully remembered or thankfully forgotten. It is carried because nobody taught us how to deal with it and because the common wisdom is firstly, that it's too painful to process it and secondly, that time heals!

Most people's experience of flower remedies starts with hearing about, or being given, Rescue Remedy for stress. Rescue Remedy is a powerful agent in circumstances of strain or upset. To experience the effect personally is to become aware of the power that a flower essence has to change negative emotions.

To move further into the practice and personal use of flower essences, firstly through the Bach system, and then through other systems such as the Bailey, Crystal Herbs, Findhorn, Australian Bush, FES, Desert Alchemy, or Masters is to proceed on the journey of life in a Rolls-Royce at a comfortable speed rather than slogging through emotional trials on foot with blisters, torn socks and holes in your boots!

I am a general practitioner in Chard, Somerset, UK. My philosophy is to provide the best of orthodox medicine to my patients and also to use complementary approaches where appropriate. Empowerment of the individual is the keystone of my approach, seeking to work with the 'patient' as a partner. For the past five years flower essences have formed an invaluable aid to my practice of medicine, as they help a person gently heal any aspects of emotion or personality that may be out of balance.

My use of flower essences in practice has grown steadily and reflects the personal use I make of them both for myself and for family and friends. They have been powerful tools to help me initially with stress and then on the journey of life.

This book is the distillation of my experience with flower essences and the use of the powerful technique of Emotional Stress Release on myself, my family and the wider circle of my friends in Chard – many of whom are also my patients. They have helped me to learn all I know. They would wish their positive experiences to be shared widely to help others, and have encouraged the writing of this book.

The *Lazy Person's Guide to Emotional Healing* is the book to help you embark on an easy journey to emotional well-being. It is dedicated to the shining soul within each of us.

It is aimed at helping each of us to empty our own Emotional Dustbin. 'I lifted the lid of the Dustbin of Life ... and looked out ...'

Chapter 1
The Emotional Dustbin

Sturt Desert Rose

In the tall Pampas grasses of South America lived a tribe of lost and confused pygmies. Their name echoed the tragedy of their lives – the 'Where-the-hell-are-we?' tribe. The grass on the plain was six feet tall. But the tallest of the tribe was only four feet high and none of them had either intuition or a sense of direction. The life of the tribe was spent running around in small circles muttering 'Where-the-hell-are-we?'

One day an elder of the tribe got the bright idea of standing on the shoulders of his friend. This instantly lifted him above the sea of grass and gave him a vision of a new place. For the first time he got a glimpse of the meaning of 'destination' and 'journey'. By holding the vision and taking periodic checks on progress he was able to lead the whole tribe safely to higher ground where the grass was much shorter – shorter than even the smallest person among them. From that day forward the individual members of the tribe could decide on their own destinations and journeys, empowered by their leap out of the sea of overwhelming grass. The tribe abandoned their former name and called themselves the 'We-know-where-we're-going' tribe – transformed into happy and confident individuals.

Humanity, trapped in the tall grass ...

Health and Disease

Health is harmony of mind, body and spirit, a sense of wholeness. The journey to good health involves going with the flow, instead of resisting it, and releasing the blockages that cause turbulence and disharmony. Disease, or dis-ease, is the opposite of health. It means 'not being at ease', a state of disharmony in mind, body, or spirit.

The purpose of the healing arts is therefore threefold: to cure disease, to restore health, and to create shining souls of radiant well-being.

Major advances in health over the next twenty years will result, not from expensive hi-tech advances in surgery and therapeutics, but from individuals taking responsibility for their own health. This represents a fundamental shift from the 'I don't care about my body – someone else will fix it when it's broken' approach to 'I do care about my body and my mind and I'm going to do all I can to stay in good health.' It reflects a societal shift in thinking, from a short-term reactive approach to a much more fruitful, long-term, proactive approach to life and the opportunities it presents. Such an approach can only be sustained by a clear sense of vision.

A sense of vision will lead us from stress, sadness and despondency towards that haven which is at the core of each of us. What stops us being our real selves? *We* do. If we try, we can all touch and hold on to the calm, peaceful, contented island that is our birthright. What usually happens is that we mistake the sea of emotions that surrounds us for reality. The grass is too tall. We have no vision and we are tossed about by waves of emotion.

If by some good fortune we have no problem emotions of our own, there's always someone ready to dump his or hers on to us. If we've managed to avoid these too, well there's always the nine o'clock news or the radio or the newspapers! But we don't have to make the 'sea of emotions' our reality. We can make our reality that tranquil island that lies within each of us. How then do we reach that island? And how do we make it free of shackles from the past, free from any misconceptions about ourselves and our relationships – in fact, free from any blockage to health and wholeness? For health and wholeness *is* that Island of Harmony, and the Sea of Emotion is one of the biggest obstacles to remembering the Island.

We live in a world governed by left-brained materialist thinking and talents. To fulfil our potential we need to allow our right-brained spiritual talents of vision, love, healing, intuition and creativity to develop fully in order to complement those left-brain talents already present. Until this happens each of us is still in disharmony and thus prey to dis-ease. What is stopping us? – the emotional wave that enfolds us all, and society's persistent denial of the very existence of spiritual talents.

There is now a great thirst for spirituality, for attaining inner peace –
and to attain it, a great need to heal the emotions. The events and
publicly-expressed feelings in the weeks following the death of Diana,
Princess of Wales, in 1997, showed us that it is okay to care, to love
unconditionally, to be vulnerable, to look inside ourselves and uncover
our emotions. It is also okay to heal our emotions, to process them,
to feel the fear and do it anyway.

Fear and Guilt

Each of us is more or less in a prison of conditioning, a prison of guilt
and emotion, a prison where fear is the lock and love is the key. Fear
is a useful warning device to help the body avoid danger. The trouble
is we've let it get out of perspective over the generations, and we've
bought the concept of fear hook, line and sinker. We've unconsciously
and unwittingly allowed fear to condition us, to dominate us and to
direct our lives. What we must learn is that fear is now redundant as
an everyday emotion. It can be released. The universal flow of the
cosmos is unconditional love, and fear is the restrictive opposite of
love. There is a continuous flow of unfolding progress in the universe,
and the release of blockages within us allows us to spiral ever upwards.
On the other hand, holding on to them means we spiral downwards.

Many of us are conditioned and driven at a deep level by feelings
of guilt, of worthlessness. Perhaps a parent once told us we weren't
'good enough' and our subconscious registered this as truth. Thus we
feel low self-esteem, a lack of love for ourselves, for our own soul and
for the temple of the body we inhabit. This blocks our progress. Stuck
in the tall Pampas grass, we wallow despondently, hurt or angry,
lacking both insight into our predicament and the vision to extract
ourselves from it. Some of us are so intensely governed by these
feelings that we project them outwards as anger, bitterness, intolerance
or even hatred. Or we make our love small and conditional. A mother
once said to her child, 'If you don't stop doing that, I won't love you
any more.' The child replied with the wisdom that only children can
muster: 'Mummy, whatever you do, I won't stop loving you.'

The true root of much of our emotional stress and imbalance is a lack
of recognition, respect and unconditional love for ourselves, at one

level or another. This causes a blockage, a turbulence in the flow of the universal energy we call love, and so disharmony and eventually disease ensue. Many people do try to love their neighbour. But the Second Commandment actually says, 'Love thy neighbour as thyself.' Loving yourself is a strong basis from which to love another. Otherwise, what professes to be outward love may actually hide self-repression and denial of our own needs. The proper flow of energy creates a harmonious circle or spiral.

Taking back your Power

Responsibility can be looked at as two words: *response* and *ability*. We each have the ability to choose our own response to every event or circumstance. We can choose between tolerance or irritation, for instance. This gift is called *free will*. It gives us the freedom at each moment to choose our response. Many would deny this, but such denial springs from conditioning, from parents, school or society, and it serves to rob us of our power.

Owning your own will is the equivalent of taking back your power. Using your free will with love and wisdom will always guide you to the correct choice. There is no real right or wrong, just a universal flow of events or a blockage to that flow. If life shows flow and joy, all is well. Change and flow are laws of the universe, but many of us resist change from a deep feeling of insecurity. Change is natural. My grandfather, born in 1903, ploughed with horses before the first world war, worked with a tractor before the second, and later again saw men land on the moon. All of this in one lifetime! If we just allow and accept change rather than resist it, we free up a tremendous amount of energy for other uses, and we release a lot of emotional tension.

The Universal Law of Attraction

Denying that we have free will or personal responsibility for ourselves goes hand-in-hand with ignoring the law of attraction. We all know the law of attraction: you get back what you give out; you reap as you sow. This is known as the law of karma. But how many of us realise that it applies not just to the physical world, but to the world of emotions too?

Half way on the road from Bristol to Bath sat an old man. A traveller from Bath stopped to ask him what the people were like in Bristol, where he was bound. 'What are they like where you were last?' asked the old man. 'Mean, nasty, low, vicious people in Bath,' replied the traveller. 'I'm sure you'll find the same wherever you go,' said the old man.

The traveller departed, a scowl on his face. Not long afterwards from the other direction came another man. 'Good day, old man. I'm on my way from Bristol to Bath,' he said, 'What are the people like in Bath?' In response the old man asked how he found Bristolians. 'Delightful, charming and generous,' smiled the second traveller. 'I'm sure you'll find the same in Bath,' replied the old man.

There are three groups of people in life, the 1 per cent, the 19 per cent and the 80 per cent. This again illustrates the awesome power of the law of attraction, or the law of return, as it is sometimes called.

The 19 per cent get up in the morning and think, 'It's going to be a dreadful day', or 'Not another dreadful day!' Unfortunately the subconscious ignores the 'not'. What, under the law of return, do you suppose the 19 per cent get back? Quite right, a dreadful day!

The 80 per cent get up with no great conscious purpose other than to survive the day. They are reactive, not pro-active people, with houses, jobs and chores to occupy them. However, written on their subconscious is, 'Life is a struggle, and sometimes it's a good day, sometimes a bad one.' So what do you think they get back, under the law of return? That's right, struggle and some days good, some days bad.

The 1 per cent get up and set the tone for their lives by affirmations of positive statements and intentions such as 'I am loving and loved and lovable', 'Everything happens in the perfect space-time sequence for me', 'Change is a natural part of my life. I welcome change for the opportunities it brings me for growth.' Any guesses as to how well their days go?

The rub is that we each have free will at every moment to choose which group we wish to be in. Modern scientific research has confirmed the fact that positive thinking helps the immune system and boosts our powers of self-healing. However, many of us act as if we were blissfully unaware of the laws of attraction and free will. To compound the problem, few have any knowledge of the emotional healing process. We learned our tables, our reading and writing, but nobody thought – or knew – to teach us about emotional healing. We only learned the clichés, 'Stiff Upper Lip', 'Bury It' or at best 'Time Heals'.

Broken Glass

Every action in life has a physical and an emotional component; getting up, eating breakfast, shopping and work. Emotions involved with most of these are processed quickly, even instantaneously, through the Accept-Acknowledge-Forgive-Release-Move on sequence of resolution. Don't forget that the Forgive element has to be achieved in three ways – towards the event, towards the other person and towards yourself for feeling the way you do.

We all get stuck on the big ones like death, divorce, job loss or other major life events. Naturally the emotional healing process is slower for these, but the same principles still apply. Unfortunately, unaware of the process of healing or of the tools which can help us, most of us are thrown back on time as a healer, and we often get stuck at some stage or other.

Sarah has been divorced twice and still holds resentment and bitter memories of both her ex-husbands. She wonders why she keeps getting ill, and why her friends are not keen to enjoy her negative feelings. Whom does her resentment hurt most? Whose powers of self-healing are crippled by this? Only her own. Mere conscious awareness of the healing process can help you through a trauma, but there are also tools to speed it up and ease it painlessly.

If you were given a handful of broken glass, what would you do? Drop it of course! Given a heartful of emotional broken glass, what do most of us do? Hide it, hold it, bury it or 'return it to sender'. Anything rather than process it, to transform and release it.

Many of us keep emotional broken glass from this year, last year or even 20 years ago, unprocessed, held out like an open sore, or tucked away in a pocket, or hidden deep in a secret drawer. Given its toxic effects on the body's powers of self-healing, why do we do this? Good question! There's no answer other than denial or being unaware of the importance of processing it.

If we choose, we can learn and apply these laws of flow, attraction and the emotional healing process to ourselves. In so doing, we free up a tremendous amount of energy for other purposes and for our body's benefit.

Self-Awareness

Observation and detachment are the final keys to the structure. Insight into our own needs is difficult; many of us in fact do not recognise our emotional and spiritual needs. Detachment is a skill that does not come naturally. It needs developing. Fortunately yet again life helps. A ship or a building can only be built by people with appropriate skills, materials and plans, and those plans result from the use of imagination, calculation and intention. Thus a physical reality comes into being from the application of thought, imagination and intention. In the same way, life's events mirror every bit of thought, imagination or intention we choose to project. When you think about it, that gives us pretty awesome power.

It also gives us pretty awesome responsibility! Scary? Not really. The word responsibility gives us the clue again. Remember, responsibility can be divided in two: response and ability. We each have the ability to choose our own response at every moment. In this way we continually contribute to the creation of our own reality.

If we can simply calm ourselves for a few moments and detach ourselves from the emotional charge of a situation, then we can begin to observe. The more we observe, the more detached we become. Eventually every moment becomes an observation of self, yet merging into the intensity of reality – a veritable waking meditation. This is detached involvement.

Sometimes people are surrounded by clouds of emotion. Sensitive individuals with the ability to 'see' describe the aura of such people as containing a lot of swirling, muddy colours. When we are in this muddy state we feel jangly or irritable. We may deal harshly with loved ones or colleagues, as these jangling emotions or tinges of sadness literally colour our approach to the world outside ourselves. And, of course, under the law of universal return we reap exactly and precisely what we sow; we get back what we give out.

Flower Essences: Tools of Transformation

So, are there any ways in which we can extract ourselves from the mud and mire of our emotional turmoil and help ourselves perform well, even excellently, no longer handicapped by our emotional imbalances? The answers depend on the causes. It is not my intention here to explore causes such as external structure of life (trying to work 90 hours a week, run a family and a business all at the same time; there are many books such as *The Seven Habits of Highly Effective People* to help you sort out the structure). Neither do I intend to explore chemical or nutritional problems or the effect of food additives on mood. Nor will I dwell on geopathic stress, spiritual bankruptcy, lack of physical life-energy, or its imbalance. These are all important, indeed vital, but outside the scope of this volume. My intention is to provide an easy introduction to a very gentle yet effective therapy – flower essences.

There are a number of ways to achieve equilibrium, all of which complement each other. Some are easy, some not so easy. Meditation, counselling, yoga, t'ai ch'i, breathing techniques, aura cleansing, prayer and devotion are all valuable tools. But for many of us one of the easiest, yet most powerful ways, is to use flower essence therapy. User-friendly, inexpensive and requiring no special training, flower essences bring us gently back into harmony with ourselves. The veritable explosion in flower remedy therapy over the past ten years is only the first swallow of summer compared to the exciting advances that are fast approaching us.

Chapter 2
The Laziest Chapter
in the Book

Honeysuckle

If you read only one chapter in this book, please read this one.
It makes emotional healing as easy as possible, by describing two
easy techniques: First, do-it-yourself flower essence combinations
comprising the widely available Bach or English flower essences,
and second, emotional stress release, a powerful do-it-yourself
kinesiology technique.

Ask a hundred adults how they feel. They will nearly all say 'Fine.'
Yet below the surface there is often a veritable torrent of chaotic
emotions. This is true for all of us, because part of the mind's way
of coping is to bury or put off the resolution of powerful emotions
that are 'too hot to handle'. So if we want to actually heal ourselves,
it is well worth while to be proactive, i.e. to search for areas of
ourselves that deserve healing, and to keep searching and searching
until no wound is left.

I can now admit that I am an addict to this process. I've been taking
flower essences daily for at least five years and I keep finding more
bits to heal. Of course I may still have occasional crabby days, but
the journey of healing and releasing baggage I didn't even realise I was
carrying, let alone the stuff I knew was there, has added a tremendous
extra dimension to the journey of life. Try it and see for yourself!

Flower Essence Combinations

It is well known that emotional imbalances can contribute not just to
emotional pain but also to physical illness. Books such as *Heal Thyself*
by the visionary Dr Edward Bach in the 1930s showed the way to
recovery. More recently Professor Candace Pert's work in the USA on
the opiate receptor, chronicled in her eminently readable *Molecules
of Emotion*, and Dr Dean Ornish's *Love and Survival, the Scientific*

Basis for the Healing Power of Intimacy have shown scientific proof for the importance of emotional balance and emotional expression, rather than bottling up our feelings, denying them, clinging to them or hiding them.

For good health, it is vital to dissolve our negative emotions and express ourselves as positively as possible. Babies *always* express their emotions freely. If they're cold they cry, if they're hungry they cry, if they have a soiled nappy they cry. Adults *rarely* express *their* emotions. Instead they tend to engage in a sort of constipation of emotions, a series of emotional blockages which pile up, layer upon layer.

From childhood our spontaneity steadily shuts down to conform with the expectations of others. How many times as children do we hear *No, Shouldn't, Can't?* To this add the possibility of abuse, so common even in families, be it physical, emotional or sexual. Then many of us have suffered bereavements, divorces, the break-up of relationships, the effects of affairs, alcoholism or drug abuse. And if you ask most adults in the street how they are, what do they say? 'Fine!' Fine!!! The conventional answer underlines the fact that most of us don't even want to acknowledge the buried pain we all carry; because we accept it as normal!

Flower essences are powerful vibrational catalysts to transform negative emotions into positive. They are emotional nutrients. By taking essences appropriate to the emotional aspect that is out of balance, transformation can occur. 'Emotional broken glass' that has been unresolved for years can be relatively swiftly transformed. For instance, Holly transforms jealousy, envy, suspicion and greed into a loving aspect, as I found out over just three days in my two-year-old who was suffering from toddler jealousy.

Here is another example: My two eldest children were tired in the last few weeks of term and had started becoming quite nasty to each other and generally touchy. Australian Adol Essence combination changed them both in three days. It is always a joy to see how rapidly children respond to a well chosen remedy. The beauty of Adol Essence, as with other combinations, is that it does what its name suggests. Additionally, Adol Essence contains some ten different flower essences, thus helping in a very wide spectrum of problems. Adol Essence is useful for issues of communication, relationships and self-worth for people of all ages, not just teenagers. Most adults benefit from a course of it, to help resolve issues either current or left over from childhood, as do most adults from a course of Relationship and Confid Essence.

Essences are to be used *not instead* of conventional therapies such as anti-depressants, counselling and so on, and do not work in every case. However, they do provide a valuable tool for the practitioner, and for all of us.

Choosing essences is the difficult bit, so here are some hints:
If nothing else, try taking Relationship Mix for 6-8 weeks, followed by Follow Your Heart Mix.

Relationship Mix: Beech, Chicory, Gentian, Heather, Holly, Impatiens, Mustard, Pine, Red Chestnut, Sweet Chestnut, Vine, Walnut, Willow. For clear, honest communication and forgiveness.

Bitch Mix: Beech, Cherry Plum, Holly, Impatiens, Pine, Vine and Willow. For irritability, whether in the case of premenstrual tension or for any wish to dominate and control or for jealousy, negativity and bitterness, or resentment.

Confidence Mix: Agrimony, Centaury, Chestnut Bud, Gentian, Larch, Pine, Sweet Chestnut, Walnut, Wild Rose. Builds inner confidence and constancy.

Study and Intuition Mix: Cerato, Chestnut Bud, Clematis, Impatiens, Rock Water, Scleranthus, Vervain, White Chestnut and Wild Oat. On occasion Wild Rose may be added. Helps you focus, concentrate and study effectively with enthusiasm and without inner distractions.

Bereavement Mix: Chestnut Bud, Gentian, Gorse, Heather, Honeysuckle, Mustard, Pine, Star of Bethlehem, Sweet Chestnut, Walnut, Wild Rose and Willow. Grief (Bailey Essences). Valuable for all who have been bereaved, even in the distant past, or for past or present negative experiences. Also for the many changes we all face in life.

11

Carer's and Worry Mix: Agrimony, Centaury, Gentian, Heather, Oak, Red Chestnut and White Chestnut. Induces tranquillity For sleeplessness add Vervain. Carers often carry a heavy burden for a long time, both emotionally and physically, so Exhaustion Mix is an ideal accompaniment to this mix, to refresh and regenerate.

Exhaustion Mix: Elm, Gorse, Hornbeam, Mustard, Oak, Olive, Walnut and Wild Rose. Useful as a pick-me-up after prolonged effort; also for those with responsibilities that sometimes become too heavy.

Addictions Mix: Agrimony, Cherry Plum, Crab Apple, Clematis, Gentian, Larch, Pine, Rock Rose, Star of Bethlehem, Walnut, White Chestnut, Wild Rose. NB This mixture will usually need Relationship Mix to follow. Helps break psychological dependencies by strengthening emotional reserves. Insecurity is one of the deep reasons for the development of addictions. The small child overcomes this problem by sucking its thumb. Unfortunately, it is not cool for adults to do this, so they often adopt more harmful habits.

Fears and Nightmares Mix: Aspen, Cherry Plum, Mimulus, Rock Rose, Star of Bethlehem, White Chestnut and Fears (Bailey Essences). For fears, terrors and nightmares, both in adults and children.

Work Stress Mix: Gentian, Hornbeam, Impatiens, Mustard, Oak, Olive, Rock Water, Vervain, Walnut, White Chestnut and Tranquillity (Bailey). Refreshes and restores interest when stressed at work. Rescue Remedy and equivalents are also useful.

Assertiveness in Leadership Mix: Agrimony, Centaury, Cerato, Chestnut Bud, Elm, Holly, Impatiens, Oak, Red Chestnut, Rock Rose, Star of Bethlehem, Walnut and Willow.

Understanding and Balance in Leadership Mix: Beech, Cerato, Chestnut Bud, Heather, Holly, Impatiens, Oak, Rock Water, Scleranthus, Star of Bethlehem, Vervain, Vine, Walnut and Wild Oat.

Follow Your Heart Mix: Centaury, Cerato, Chestnut Bud, Pine, Rock Water, Wild Oat. To help us follow our intuition and the path in life that is best for us, even if it is not obvious at present. Also helps us gain wisdom from life's experiences.

Blues Mix: Gentian, Gorse, Mustard, Sweet Chestnut, Walnut, Wild Rose, Willow, Despair (Bailey). Helps lift low moods and sadness; allows the sunshine back into life. Not instead of conventional anti-depressants if advised by a medical practitioner.

Past Abuse Mix: Agrimony, Crab Apple, Gentian, Gorse, Holly, Mustard, Pine, Rock Rose, Star of Bethlehem, Sweet Chestnut, Walnut, Willow, Childhood and Grief (Bailey). Useful for cases of past emotional, physical and sexual abuse. Australian Bush Sexuality Essence would be useful as well, for sexual abuse.

Insomnia Mix: Impatiens, Olive, Rock Rose, Vervain and White Chestnut. Useful for releasing mental and emotional patterns and excitement that prevents refreshing sleep.

Many health food shops will now make up a combination such as one of the above for a fixed price, making it very economical to use flower essences.

Alternatively, choose a combination essence already made up from the Australian Bush or other ranges from Chapter 6.

During and after taking these combinations you may notice profound changes in yourself. You may notice that all sorts of forgotten or painfully remembered past events come to mind, only in a different light, a more comfortable light. You may experience the shedding of long-repressed tears. A variety of emotions may be released from deep within you and come to the surface to be acknowledged and released as the emotional memory banks are cleansed and healed.

The following is the best description I know of this process:

> The suggestion of using Bach Flower Remedies to treat what might be the underlying cause of my back pain at first seemed novel and different. Although I agreed to give them a try I was very sceptical. They had been around since the 1930s and were developed by a physician with a Harley Street practice, so why wasn't every doctor prescribing them? I liked the idea of trying to treat the real problem rather than the symptoms of pain in my back, particularly where the consultant anaesthetist had difficulties inserting the epidural for the caesarean delivery of my daughter.
>
> To begin with, the remedies (Mustard and Walnut) did not seem to be having a noticeable effect but I was also taking pain-killing tablets. Then I began to notice that various events or occasions in my life would come to mind. Often I would rethink these occasions, see what was really good in them for me, and I would feel much more at ease with the thoughts.
>
> This happened not only to the good memories but to the bad ones as well. It was as if someone had opened the emotional filing cabinet, and no way could I close it. Gradually I have found incident after incident coming to mind for reassessment – memories which at one time I could never have faced again. Memories which I could not under any circumstances have shared with anyone could now be dealt with and put away. Pandora's box of personal memories was revealing the bad things. Gradually each was being cleaned away.
>
> In this process I learned to really cry again and not to withhold my feelings and batten them down. When I was a child, my mother had insisted that my father never saw me in tears, but now the tears could flow

> freely. There was no guilt feeling about crying now. As the gentle cleansing and healing process has gone on over the weeks I have begun to realise that I am still an attractive woman with a lot to contribute to the world I live in. The whole effect seems to me to be rather like an old Dutch master's portrait which has become grimy and soiled with time and with smoke from the fire. When it is gently cleaned and restored with modern techniques the beauty of the picture is almost better than in its original state; the lights and tones shine through much more clearly; the subtle hues and highlights become more apparent.

To make up a dropper bottle, fill a 30ml dropper bottle with 9 parts fresh (not boiled) water and 1 part brandy or vodka, just to preserve the mixture. Next, put 3 drops of each of your chosen remedies into your dosage bottle, taking care to hold the dropper above the level of your dosage bottle rim. Combination essences such as the Australian should be taken straight from the bottle. Replace the dropper on the stock bottle, finger tight. When you have put all the remedies in, replace the top, hold the bottle and bless it, perhaps asking that it should work for your highest good, at full potency, and without any untoward effects. Your treatment bottle is now ready to use. Without licking the dropper, drop 2 or 3 drops of your remedies on to your tongue. Repeat 4-6 times daily for up to 4-6 weeks.

Good Luck !

Compatibility and Side Effects

Flower essences are compatible with all allopathic and complementary medicines. On occasion, allopathic, homeopathic, herbal or other approaches may be more appropriate than essence therapy. Side effects are rare and generally limited to intolerance to the brandy or vodka carrier. These may be headaches, nausea or heartburn, each of which I have seen, albeit rarely. A few individuals, when starting essence therapy, have headaches. The mechanism of this is possibly that many of us carry a large load of toxic emotions, chemicals, and nutritional imbalances. When a healing process is first initiated by a catalyst such as a flower essence, the body heaves a sigh of relief and exhibits symptoms of release, just as some people work flat out all week, then wonder why they get a migraine at the weekend. Of course, it is only when your foot is taken off the accelerator pedal that you can hear the rattles that you have been able to ignore. Nausea and heartburn appear to occur only in people who may be intolerant to brandy in particular, or to alcohol in general. To minimise these effects, either slow down your rate of taking the essences, or put them on to the front of your wrists directly from the stock bottle.

Another seeming side effect is a change in emotional state for the worse, perhaps towards crying or agitation, or the experiencing of a buried or unresolved emotion such as grief. If you experience this, it is worth taking time to look quietly at the emotions that are surfacing, for usually they hold a clue as to their origin. They are coming from within, often from long-forgotten depths. Take time and reflect quietly on the meaning of these emotions to you, and the wisdom they may bring you as they resolve. A friend to discuss issues or support you may be helpful; also, changing the dosage rate to just once a day, perhaps at a quiet time such as evening, can be of benefit. As submerged feelings surface, occasionally causing turmoil, one of the Rescue or Emergency Essences may be needed for a short while. Walnut and Chestnut Bud are also useful stabilisers to take. This is not so much a side effect as a healing crisis of buried emotions that are surfacing. Most people never experience this phenomenon, but it is well to be aware of it.

NB Health Warning: To use flower essences proactively rather than just when you feel you need help can seriously change your life and allow the miraculous to become commonplace for you! Especially if you read some of Stuart Wilde's books, James Redfield's *The Celestine Vision* and Eileen Caddy's *Opening Doors Within*! My own life has changed phenomenally, yet smoothly and with no major problems. Flower essences have enabled me to just 'go with the flow'.

To move further into the practice and personal use of flower remedies, for example through the Bach system, and then perhaps the Bailey,

Crystal Herbs, Findhorn, Australian Bush, FES, Desert Alchemy or other systems, is to proceed on the journey of life in a Rolls-Royce at a comfortable speed rather than slogging through the emotional trails of life on foot with blisters, torn socks and holes in your boots.

Emotional Stress Release

The power of the mind-body is far beyond the comprehension of those of us brought up to believe that if you can't see or feel it, it can't be true !

Kinesiology, a treatment modality developed by Brian Butler, can help rebalance the mind-body in many ways. Here we will concentrate on one technique only, ESR or Rapid Memory Healing. Research into this incredibly simple technique was started by the observation that many people, when stressed, place their hand on their forehead.

> Oscar, a retired professional, had consulted me at various times over 6 years. He had never admitted to me, or possibly to anyone else, that he saw bombs falling every day. Oscar was not mad; far from it. In 1945 he had been on a troop-ship in the Indian Ocean when the ship was dive-bombed. Ever since then he had been haunted by a traumatic and painful memory.
>
> He healed that memory in two minutes, never to be troubled by it again. Fifty years of pain healed in two minutes! Six months later, he had not been troubled by the memory again. How was this done? Simple. By placing a hand on his forehead and reliving the memory. Nothing more, nothing less.

Placing a hand on the forehead gives the mind the opportunity to release any trapped emotion that had neither outlet nor resolution at the moment of the original incident – because the original emotion was either suppressed, denied or too painful to be dealt with at the time.

It was the subconscious mind's way of best coping. The problem arises when the memory is never healed, or never given the opportunity to heal. In this case, what often happens is that it keeps returning to mind, sometimes as flashbacks or nightmares.

Back to the technique. In more detail, you place your hand on your forehead, of course sitting quietly with no deadlines or distractions. Your intention is to heal a single traumatic memory; not a whole string, but just one. Trying to do too many at a time may result in overload, just as trying to heal a recent one that relates closely to a whole lot of unhealed issues may also not work, by dredging up too much at once.

Next, close your eyes. Allow the memory that needs to be healed to come into your mind. This is not a problem. Generally the challenge is to keep all the others out! What happens next is very interesting. Usually the incident suddenly becomes very real, even intensely real, portrayed in vivid colours. For a few seconds, generally up to ten, but on rare occasions for up to 30 seconds, it becomes more intense as the original unreleased pain is allowed expression. You may experience tears, sobs or sighs as expressions of the release of the trapped emotion.

Then, gradually at first, and increasingly more rapidly, as you continue to concentrate on the memory, it fades. You keep concentrating until you are no longer able to bring the incident back to mind. The emotion just dissolves, and resolves, forever.

> Frances's flatmate had been stabbed in front of her, in their flat. Though he soon got over the physical trauma, she was unable to erase the shock of the memory from her mind. It would often return to her, and eventually the relationship broke up. Using this technique resolved her anguish and emotional pain, but not until five years had passed since the incident. Taking it a little further from the 'resolved position', and keeping concentrating on it, hand on forehead, Frances was then able to describe the incident as 'Yellow and fluffy, no longer painful in any way'.

Top: *Giant Protea (South African Creativity Essence)*

Bottom: *Disa (South African Crisis Essence)*

Sugar Bush Protea (South African Inner Child Essence)

It seems that we have within us an ability to process and heal emotional trauma buried deep in the mind; and the clue is in the unconscious gesture of hand-on-forehead. All we have to do is to use the gesture proactively. Personally I have found it useful at the end of every day, to release any clutter I pick up. It has also been used to heal the large segments of childhood, teenage or job memories – broken up, of course, into bite-sized chunks! Sometimes it is helpful whilst one hand is on your forehead to have the other touching your back at the base of the spine, a very grounding manoeuvre.

Some people find that, the first few times they try this technique, it is difficult to focus on a single chosen memory. Don't worry, this may mean there are lots of unhealed memories clamouring for attention. They can be healed only one at a time, so try to focus on the most persistent memory, or alternatively take a few doses of Clematis, Scleranthus, Walnut and White Chestnut, which should help you to concentrate and focus when you try the ESR again.

If only we could examine the neurotransmitter pathways in the brain whilst this process is underway!

Chapter 3
What are Flower Essences?

Crowea

Flower essences are tools of transformation, catalysts for change. They are the essences of flowers captured in water. They contain a healing vibration that catalyses change and enables transformation on emotional, mental and spiritual levels.

The words 'essence' or 'remedy' are used interchangeably because they refer to the essence or healing vibration of the plant. This becomes the remedy or healing agent for the imbalance that is present.

Flower essences are used because they help us to feel better. They work to heal us primarily on emotional and mental levels and to restore harmony.

We shall start with a story from my own practice, using Rescue Remedy, the flower essence everybody knows.

> John's wife was in hospital in intensive care. She had just had a caesarean section for toxaemia of pregnancy. She was unwell but her condition was not critical. John, on the other hand was at home in a state of complete panic. He was sitting in a corner of his sofa, looking at the floor, mumbling, 'She's going to die. It's going to be awful. What will I do? She's going to die. It's going to be awful. What will I do? She's going to die. It's going to be awful. What will I do?' He sat there, shrunken, pale, looking much older than his 30 years.
>
> His mother had been comforting him for several hours. She now put three drops of Rescue Remedy into a glass of water. He sipped it, not because he knew what it was but because he was told to do so. 'She's going to die. It's going to be awful. What will I do?' Sip. Sip. He

sipped the glass every 30 seconds. Initially there was no change, but after 4 minutes the tone of voice changed. The words were the same but there was less conviction in his voice. Sip. Sip. Almost imperceptibly, he changed. By the end of 10 minutes the litany of woe had stopped. He stood up for the first time, dried his eyes and said, 'Well, there's no point in moping about crying here. Why don't I ring the hospital, find out how she is and go and see her?'

John was better, fully in control of himself again. Next day he bought six bottles of Rescue Remedy, one for each room in the house including the bathroom. Perhaps he missed the point on dosage, but he was certainly convinced it worked.

That was the most dramatic instance I have ever seen of Rescue Remedy working. But was it all in the mind? Was it a placebo effect?

A Placebo?

Isabel was two and she loved her new baby sister Rose. When Rose was three months old the love became somewhat weaker and quickly turned to jealousy. Some of you may have had the privilege of the experience of living with toddler jealousy. This is a phenomenon where a previously normal child turns into a whining, manipulative, hateful, jealous little monster. You will know that at the three-week stage you have read the books, done all the right things, been kind and supportive and followed all the right advice. You will also know that none of it works.

In the little leaflet on Bach Remedies, against the words jealousy, envy, revenge, suspicion and greed, appears

> the remedy Holly. So, into Isabel's little red beaker went three drops of Holly essence with every drink. To her the beaker was no different. Within two days she had changed into a loving little angel, her true and better nature restored.

Isabel hadn't heard of the placebo effect, even if she had noticed what went into her beaker. This episode proved to me that, although there may be a placebo effect for adults choosing their own remedies, for children there is none. It also proved that flower remedies work very quickly on children.

Rescue Remedy is widely used on the dog show circuit and at a local animal sanctuary. The effects on animals are often transformational, calming anxious or aggressive animals or dissolving the effects of shock.

Dr Edward Bach's Theory of Health

The name Dr Edward Bach is almost synonymous with flower remedies. He is the father of modern flower remedy therapy. A bacteriologist, homeopath and Harley Street physician, he trained in London, qualifying in 1912. A keen observer of human character, in 1930 he formulated his theory of the causation of disease in a slim but incisive volume entitled *Heal Thyself*.

He proposed that a symptom complex, or disease, was the end-result in the physical body of a conflict whose origins were to be found in the emotional, mental and spiritual disharmonies that arise for an individual. He stated that, though treating the physical symptoms with material means might be of value, no cure would come about unless the deeper conflicts were addressed. Dr Bach championed Hahnemann, the founder of homeopathy, as being an exception to 'modern materialism' – whatever that was in 1930. Hahnemann, he felt, realised 'the love of the Creator and the Divinity which resides within man' and used God-given plants and natural remedies to enable the life force or Inner Healer to throw off a disease.

Bach further proposed five points about the cause of illness. These points are found again and again in much modern philosophy and mind-body-spirit thinking.

1. The physical body is the earthly temple or physical vehicle for the higher self or soul. The soul is our real self and a reflection of the divine.

2. We are each a personality who, for our lifetime, dons a physical body. The purpose of life's journey is to gain experience and knowledge on the earth plane. Earth is an amazing workshop for our souls on their life's journey, enabling us to develop qualities and skills.

3. A single lifetime on earth is only a small, though vital, part of the development of each soul, 'as one day at school is to a life'. The soul itself is an immortal spark of the divine. It is difficult for us fully to understand these concepts.

4. Health is harmony of soul and personality or, as we would say, mind, body and spirit. From this harmony flows joy, peace and happiness. If we lose our guidance from our higher self due to our own ego or that of others muscling in, then conflict arises. Such conflict or disharmony is the root cause of disease and unhappiness. Whether rich or poor, prince or pauper, our daily life offers each of us the most appropriate lessons and opportunities for personal growth.

5. There is a universal consciousness which connects all things. Further, the creative force behind all matter is love. The creator can be imagined as a great blazing sun of love, sending rays in all directions. We and our consciousness are just particles at the tip of each beam, sent out to gain experience and knowledge, ultimately to return to the source to enrich it. We are all part of the whole.

Bach felt that there were two possible major causes of imbalance, both of which would bring disharmony and eventually disease. One is to lose touch with your inner guidance so that the personality or ego rules instead of acting in tune with your higher self. The other is to act unkindly or wrongly against another person or nature, for this would be an act against the whole. Treating others judgmentally is not useful, for other souls are at different stages of development.

However, an understanding of the error and a subsequent effort to correct the fault would lead back to health and happiness, joy and peace. Bach felt that disease was a means of showing the error of imbalance. If corrective steps were taken they would lead back to health before the last resort of pain and suffering occurred. Physicians and practitioners of the healing arts should use both physical remedies (medicine and surgery) and also give the patients the knowledge of why they have suffered and what can be done to cure the root causes. Dr Bach formulated this theory partly from his own observations and from traditions such as those of Hippocrates, Paracelsus and Hahnemann. Today we may reflect on the words 'health', which can be split into *heal-th*, and comes from the same root as *hale*, *whole* and *holistic*. The word 'disease' implies that one is not at ease.

As a homeopath and bacteriologist Bach made two crucial observations. First, that emotional, mental and spiritual imbalance creates disease. He sought from nature gentle cures to restore health by addressing these factors, first finding answers in homeopathy. It was in this field that he noticed that people could be classed into a number of different types of temperament. Furthermore, these groups of people shared similar imbalances in their gut bacteria. He first developed injectable vaccines that gave a partial relief of symptoms in these people, whatever the disease. Then, rejecting this approach as crude, he potentised his bowel flora cultures into homeopathic 'nosodes' or treatments. The Bach nosodes are still used today by homeopaths.

The second crucial insight was that, whatever the disease picture, it is the personality that should be treated, particularly when the patterns are of emotional imbalance. Dr Bach wrote, 'Take no notice of the disease. Think only of the outlook on life of the one in distress. As the individual is treated and becomes well, the disease goes, cast off by the increase in health.' He pointed out that the mind shows the pattern of illness or imbalance before the body does, and that in illness there is a change in mood away from that of normal life. Observation and early treatment of these imbalances keep the vital energy of the body high and maintain health.

Perhaps Bach dealt harshly with material or physical medicine, but he was practising just prior to the great age of pharmaceutical advances such as antibiotics. In 1930 meningitis was feared for its high mortality rate. Pneumonia would reach a 'crisis' after which the patient either died or recovered. An ear infection could lead to mastoiditis and deafness or meningitis, whilst a dirty wound from gardening or a dog bite could also be fatal. We are fortunate to be able to take for granted that in cases like these antibiotic therapy will produce a 'miracle cure'.

Dr Bach and Flower Remedies

Bach's concern to avoid adverse effects of treatment led him to abandon homeopathy and his Harley Street practice. In 1930 he left London to seek a gentler form of treatment for emotional imbalances, the true deeper causes of disease as he saw them.

First in Wales, then near Cromer in East Anglia, and lastly in Mount Vernon, Sotwell, Oxfordshire, he discovered plant after plant which answered his needs. There is no doubt that Bach, a natural healer, was also a spiritual sensitive. This gift he developed to the point where he could tell the healing properties of a flower by holding it in his hand. He himself called his remedies his *helpers*, indicating that he was aware of his healing powers.

Perhaps inspired by the sixteenth-century writings of Paracelsus, he sought the healing power of flowers. Paracelsus, sometimes called the Father of Modern Medicine, rediscovered the healing power of the morning dew on a flower. Flowers are the highest, most evolved part of a plant. They make us feel better. They bring a smile to our faces.

Bach's inquiring mind soon discovered that the power of dew from a flower in the sun was greater than that from a flower in the shade. His great innovation was to establish a method of capturing and preserving this vibration. Water is the universal carrier of vibrations, but will go stagnant in a few days. Bach hit on the idea of using sunshine to potentise quantities of water in a glass bowl rather than collecting dew-drops. Collecting dew is of course perfectly possible but rather time-consuming and tedious! The potentised water could now be preserved by mixing it in equal proportions with brandy. This is mother tincture, and it heals people.

With his homeopathic background Bach soon established that a dilution of 6 drops of mother tincture in 10ml brandy would make an effective stock strength. Such a process has the advantages of economy of effort and long-term storage. Further dilution in a similar way into a dropper bottle of water would also have sufficient healing power.

Bach developed the boiling method by which half of his remedies are prepared. This has considerable similarity to the great British herbal tradition he would have known. One remedy, Rock Water, is actually healing water taken from certain healing wells. In all cases the preservation with brandy is the same, to make mother tincture and stock essences.

Dr Edward Bach's rediscovery of an ancient system of therapy, mentioned by Paracelsus and used down the ages by aboriginals and other native tribes, was an important and momentous advance. It is entirely fitting that the original set of 38 remedies that he developed from Mother Nature should carry his name as a mark of respect.

Bach Remedies Worldwide

Dr Bach wished his 38 remedies to be used inexpensively by the lay person at home just as much as by the professional physician. He also made the method of preparation known in his *Twelve Healers and Four Helpers* (1933) so that any folk, lay or professional, might prepare the remedies to which he was proud to put his name. The 38 original remedies are now made, following the original Bach method, not only in his own locations by the Bach Centre at Mount Vernon but from identical plants in various locations, by a number of producers in Britain and overseas. They are distributed worldwide by one of the original firms with whom Dr Bach was proud to associate, A. Nelson and Co, and also by Healing Herbs, Ainsworths, Milagra, Crystal Herbs, Sun Essences, Deva, Korte PHI and a number of other producers worldwide.

The Next Stage

Bach Remedies continued to be made at Mount Vernon after his death. For a number of years they were produced but not widely known. Had it not been for the dedication of Nora Weeks and Victor Bullen, they might have disappeared altogether. But by the 1970s the Bach Remedies had helped many people and inspired Patricia Kaminski and Richard Katz to join forces to make the FES essences in the USA. Soon after that, Gurudas' book *Flower Essences and Vibrational Healing* appeared, describing a number of essences.

Steadily the number of producers has grown through the 1980s and 1990s so that, now, flower essences are produced in every continent of the world. Many gifted and talented makers hold workshops and train practitioners in the use of their essences. Some have produced a variety of educational materials and have provided detailed analyses of thousands of case studies. Courses and workshops are run throughout the world. Brazil even has a postgraduate diploma in Flower Essence Therapy at the University of Sao Paulo, whilst in the UK, universities and adult education establishments now have modules on Flower Essence Therapy.

New innovations in making essences have brought forward a number of exciting developments. Some essences are now made in vodka, rather than water, and some are potentised by moonlight. Such processes bring out different healing vibrations from the flower. Even using differing numbers of blooms can alter the character of the remedy. Essences are also made from gems, shells and other facets of Nature's bountiful creation.

What is interesting is that, although a particular essence might originate from say Britain or California, the needs of humans are similar, to the point that those essences are equally needed in New England and in Australia. Likewise essences from New Zealand, Peru or Brazil also have a global application.

The Bach remedies were developed in the 1930s and deal mainly with the basic emotional issues we all face, although there is actually tremendous depth to each of his remedies. In the past 25 years many new essences have been developed to deal with other issues and aspects of personality. Change is inevitable in life, and it would be unrealistic to expect the new essences of the 1970s and 1980s to be the only ones in common use in another twenty years. This reflects the increased pace of life, the ease of communication and travel, and increased awareness of not just the emotional issues of life but the spiritual and metaphysical ones as well.

Chapter 4
How Flower Essences Work

Waratah

Flower essences are tools for transformation, catalysts for change.

Seven-year-old Natalie kept getting headaches and stomach pains, before or during school. She had been unhappy at school: most days taking her there was a major battle. She felt vulnerable in the crowd of children at morning assembly. She wouldn't eat at school. She often cried at night.

Her teacher wrote to me asking for Natalie to be referred to a child psychiatrist as a case of 'school refusal'. The letter said, 'Natalie is a keen, intelligent girl who mixes well with her peers and has no problems with learning. She continually complains of stomach pain at school, or before coming to school in the morning. Her mother reports that Natalie does not always eat or drink properly, and that you have not found any physical cause for her problems.

'We feel that the problem could possibly stem from Natalie setting herself unrealistic goals and bringing anxieties on herself when not achieving, or thinking she does not achieve, these targets. We feel that a child psychiatrist might be able to offer some assistance in resolving the situation, and hope you can offer Natalie an appointment as soon as possible.'

Natalie's mother had previously heard of Rescue Remedy and was willing to give flower essences a try before referral for professional help. We chose the Bach remedies Gentian, Larch, Mustard, Rock Rose and Willow.

> Natalie took the remedies six times a day. Five days of this treatment brought a complete change in her. She regained her confidence and was happy at school. Her stomach pains and headaches disappeared.

- Gentian brings the quality of unshakeable confidence in difficult circumstances, dissolving despondency and depression from known challenges.

- Larch draws up full confidence from deep within, when on the surface it has evaporated to the point where one gives up trying, certain in advance of failure.

- Mustard restores happiness and joy, dissolving those sudden depressions which come on for no reason and go again just as quickly, like the shadow from a dark cloud in a blue sky.

- Rock Rose brings tremendous calm, releasing the paralysing feeling of terror that a threat can cause.

- Willow restores the quality of optimism despite challenges. The emotion that Willow dispels is that of resentment, bitterness and self-pity.

How do Flower Essences Work?

Flower essences work by enhancing the positive aspects of the qualities of mind, emotion and personality. By flooding a person with positive qualities the negative aspects or the lack of positive are dissolved, and health is restored. They are catalysts for the resolution of emotions.

We all have many qualities of emotion and personality. Dr Bach described the main 38 first-level ones. These are qualities such as love, faith, optimism in adversity, tolerance, gentleness with self, decisiveness and so on. Such qualities can be either fully present, totally lacking, or partly present. When we are healthy and all is in balance, each quality is shining out to its full potential. Of course, we are all different and possess differing measures of each quality to reflect our individual and unique make-up.

Sometimes the quality no longer shines out strongly, but becomes negative. Each quality has its opposite, or the state which occurs when the quality is absent – for nature will always fill a vacuum.

- The reverse of love is jealousy, envy, revenge, suspicion and greed, summed up in the word hatred. (Holly)

- The opposite of faith is discouragement and despondency. (Gentian)

- The counterpart of optimism in adversity is bitterness and resentment. (Willow)

- The opposite of tolerance is intolerance. (Beech)

- The reverse of decisiveness is indecision. (Scleranthus)

Flower essences put back the positive aspects of a quality, shifting us from negative to positive, or from left to right, on a graph. To understand this movement we use the analogy of a bright light shining from within us out onto the world. This light shines through different windows, each representing a particular quality. Sometimes the windows are misted up, covered with cobwebs, or the shutters are closed. Taking the appropriate remedy gradually opens the shutters, blows away the cobwebs and unmists the glass, allowing the light to shine out in full brightness again.

Sometimes the light shines out quickly again as a temporary blockage is dissolved. Sometimes it takes longer, as when the block is deeper and more long-standing. Other times, all appears well for the present, but the stain of a blockage originating five, ten, or twenty years earlier needs wiping clean. The process is exactly the same in each case; the difference is in duration and frequency of treatment.

Pamela was 49 when she wrote the following:

> The suggestion of using Bach Flower Remedies to treat what might be the underlying cause of my back pain at first seemed novel and different. Although I agreed to give them a try I was very sceptical. They had been around since the 1930s and were developed by a physician with a Harley Street practice, so why wasn't every doctor prescribing them? I liked the idea of

trying to treat the real problem rather than the symptoms of pain in my back, particularly where the consultant anaesthetist had had difficulties inserting the epidural for the caesarean delivery of my daughter many years previously.

To begin with, the Essences (Mustard and Walnut) did not seem to be having a noticeable effect, but I was also taking pain-killing tablets. Then I began to notice that various events or occasions in my life would come to mind. Often I would rethink these occasions, see what was really good in them for me and feel much more at ease with the thoughts.

This happened not only to the good memories but to the bad ones as well. It was as if someone had opened the emotional filing cabinet and no way could I close it. Gradually I have found incident after incident coming to mind for reassessment – memories which at one time I could never have faced again. These memories which I could not under any circumstances have shared with anyone, could now be dealt with and put away. Pandora's Box of personal memories was revealing the bad things and gradually each was being cleaned away.

In this process I learned to really cry again and not to withhold my feelings and batten them down. As a child my mother had insisted that my father never saw me in tears. But now the tears could flow freely. There was no longer any guilt-feeling about crying.

As the gentle cleansing and healing process went on, I began to realise that I am still an attractive woman with a lot to contribute to the world I live in.

The whole effect seems to me to be rather like an old Dutch master's portrait which has become grimy and soiled with time. When it is gently cleaned and restored with modern techniques the beauty of the picture is almost better than in its original state; the lights and tones shine through much more clearly; the subtle hues and highlights become more apparent.

What seems to be happening here for Pamela is that the emotional healing process is being traversed painlessly.

The Emotional Healing Process

The emotional healing process, or ladder of emotional healing, is well known. Simply, it is expressed as follows:

- Accept

- Acknowledge

- Forgive:
  - The other person
  - The event
  - Yourself

- Release

- Move on

The ladder (or perhaps snake) of emotional healing applies to every single event you ever experience. Every event has a mental component, an emotional component and a physical component. Getting up in the morning, going to work/school/shop, even going to the bathroom, has an emotional component. Fortunately the 'healing' of most events is automatic. Imagine having to forgive yourself every time you went to the toilet! Work/school/shops could be more of an effort. If you have queued in a supermarket on a busy Saturday you'll know that you have at least to forgive the event and release the trauma from your mind!

When we come to the big challenges, the emotional healing is more difficult. Losing a loved one, going through a divorce, moving house and changing jobs are all counted as major life events which cause stress and make serious illness more likely. Perhaps it is not so much the nature of the event as our ability to deal with its emotional component that makes major illness more likely at these times. Knowing the ladder of healing is a help in itself.

Flower essences accelerate and ease the journey through the process of healing the emotions, to the point where they could almost be called 'The Lazy Person's Tools for Healing'. Certainly many people, myself amongst them, have benefitted from the help they give in these circumstances.

Flower essences, as catalysts for change, work with us to transform us. By treating the whole person rather than just individual symptoms, an important overview appears. Flower remedies bring to our awareness aspects of disharmony within us. They support us energetically whilst we use the ladder of emotional healing to process and gently release the imbalance. From this process we gain insight into our own natures. We use these insights to gain knowledge and experience on life's journey. These insights help us take responsibility for ourselves, our actions and our state of mind.

In the Bach system, Star of Bethlehem would help with the initial shock of acceptance. For the next stages you might use Walnut and Mustard, with perhaps Pine, Gentian or Gorse as well. Forgiveness is vital, for any resentment held within your body tends to weaken the immune system and the inner healer. Willow is an important remedy at this point. Many other essences are also effective, from the Bach system and from other systems.

The Scientific Basis for Use of Flower Essences

How do flower essences work scientifically? The simple answer is through 'harmonic resonance'. Flower essences act by dissolving negative thought patterns and allowing positive harmonious vibrations to replace disharmony.

Perhaps you remember the physics experiments at school. A large bare room has two tables in it, one at each end. On each table sits a tuning fork. Both are tuned to the same frequency. Middle C perhaps? 256Hz. One tuning fork is struck and set humming. Almost immediately the other fork, at the far end of the room, picks up the vibration and resonates with an identical hum. That's how flower essences affect human beings and restore health!

But to leave the question there would be to ignore the rich treasure of scientific research that explains the likely mechanisms by which such a simple concept comes about.

Dr Bach was formulating his revolutionary theories of health and
illness in the 1920s. At the same time Einstein was rocking the world
of physics with his theory of relativity, which states that $E=mc^2$,
in other words, energy, matter and the speed of light are all related.

We tend to think that a table or a book is solid whilst a sound or
a thought is not. Yet each is merely energy or a vibrating wave form.
It is the rate or frequency of vibration that determines whether
we perceive an object to be solid or not. In fact many different
wave forms or frequencies can co-exist in the same space. For example,
our houses and even our bodies are filled with radio and television
waves at this very moment; we just can't perceive them unless we
use the right instrument.

Our beliefs about 'reality' tend to be very much coloured by what we
can touch, smell, see, hear or taste. Yet bats and dogs can hear sounds
that we can't and some people are genetically unable to taste certain
foods. If you're short-sighted like me and you lose your glasses, your
perception of reality is limited even further. Just because we are unable
to see the horizon doesn't mean that it stops existing!

As the limerick runs:

There once was a man who said 'God
Must find it exceedingly odd
If he finds that this tree
Continues to be
When there's no-one about in the Quad'

and the reply

'Dear Sir, Your astonishment's odd:
I am always about in the Quad.
And that's why the tree
Will continue to be,
Since observed by Yours Faithfully, God'

Vibrational Medicine

Dr Richard Gerber has coined the term 'Vibrational Medicine' to cover medical theory and practice based on Einstein's discoveries. It has long been recognised that we are more than just flesh and bones, more than just a pump and vessels, more than just computer and connections. Einstein shows that in fact we are coherent fields of energy, vibrating in such a way that we can feel we are discrete individuals with physical bodies, senses and consciousness.

Furthermore we possess not just a physical body but an etheric (electro-magnetic) body as well. We know that electric cables generate a magnetic field around them and that holding a fluorescent tube near a high tension electricity cable will cause it to glow. Physics tells us that we are composed of molecules, atoms, electrons and even smaller particles, each of which we know creates its own force field. So it is hardly surprising that the etheric field around us exists, just like a field around an electric cable. It's just that most of us can't see it!

Actually more and more people are starting to see the etheric as a fuzzy white glow around people, trees, or other living things. In certain lighting conditions I have seen this myself. Some gifted people can see a coloured aura around others and can tell that different emotions show up as different colours – perhaps anger as a muddy red, love as a healing pink or green.

Back to science! Dr Saxton Burr at Yale in the 1940s detected the electrical field surrounding living things. Curiously, the field around a sprouting seed was not the shape of the seed but that of the adult plant.

Dr Nordenstrom, one-time head of radiology at the Karolinska Institute in Sweden, and former Nobel Prize Committee chairman, researched the biological electrical system in the human body. He found that the system is disordered in cancer patients. In a number of cases he obtained exciting results in helping people with cancer. His extensive research is only now being taken up by the mainstream research establishment.

The Russian Semyon Kirlian took photographs of living things in the presence of a low-current, high-frequency, high-voltage electrical field.

Kirlian photographs of many living things show what appears to be an aura. Furthermore, flower essences have a definable Kirlian imprint. In some cases this imprint actually resembles the flower which made the essence. It is known that a laser photograph of a banana can be captured on film as a hologram and, through the use of a laser decoder, the original image can be projected in 3D. The hologram is a record of energy patterns. Applying Kirlian photography to part of a leaf actually produces an intact image of the whole leaf.

At quantum level, matter is literally frozen light, that is, energy fields. So matter itself is composed of energy fields, or rather is a specialised energy field. Professor David Bohm proposed that the universe is an interconnected whole. It is only in our minds that we perceive it to be separated into lots of bits. This perception is purely an illusion, comparable to the concept of 'maya', or illusion, in Eastern philosophies. Tragically this illusion colours our view of everything, leading to confusion and conflict within ourselves. If we are confused deep within, no wonder society is full of conflict, fear and confusion!

Vibrational medicine is a system in which one form of energy frequency is used to influence the underlying (or overlighting) energy structure of a body, to bring it back towards balance.

Flower Essences and Vibrational Medicine

Water is the universal carrier of vibrational imprints. The hydrogen-oxygen bonds in the H_2O molecule have an infinite number of bond-angle permutations and electron orbit shifts, even without considering sub-atomic particles, and therefore they possess an infinite capacity for carrying different vibrations. It is likely that, during the process of potentisation of flower essences in sunlight, the water starts to resonate with the vibrational imprint of the flower. This resonance then remains in the water, and can be detected by Kirlian photography.

Applying the appropriate resonant frequency (the correct flower essence) to a complex discordant wave-form (a human out of balance, in a particular mental or emotional aspect) rebalances the energy system to return order to the former chaos. This phenomenon is called entrainment. The physics experiment of placing sand on to a drum, then applying a sound, illustrates this nicely. Depending on the sound the sand quickly falls into beautifully regular patterns on the surface of the drum.

The following analogy is helpful in understanding how flower remedies fit in with the rest of medical practice.

We all play a tune which is in harmony when we are well. Our tune is like the hum of a well-performed melody on the piano. When we go out of balance the notes become jangling and discordant.

Sometimes the piano strings are broken. Surgery repairs them. Sometimes the notes stick. Orthodox medicine oils them and frees them up. The strings can be out of tune. Let homeopathy reharmonise the physical piano. But let's say the pianist is hungry and tired – flower remedies act as a tonic to refresh and uplift him or her. The result is an inspired performance! Of course there is overlap – homeopathy can have profound mental effects; antibiotic treatment of bacterial meningitis saves the piano from sinking like the *Titanic*; and surgical tracheostomy for laryngeal obstruction enables the rest of the body/mind/spirit to continue to function whilst the obstruction is dealt with.

Imagine a symphony orchestra before a concert. The audience waits, hearing only a varying cacophony of many instruments playing their own discordant notes. At a given moment the lead violin starts to tune the open string to an A. Gradually at first, then more rapidly, the entire company of assembled musicians pick up the note until a single A is being played by the whole orchestra. All are now in harmonic unison, started by a single player setting the note.

Essentially flower essences reintroduce a harmonising, healing note to the whole organism. They work on the emotional/etheric level to gently bring the whole structure back into balance. They work subtly, mediated through the electrical system of the body. They are compatible with all orthodox medicine and other vibrational medicine and though their action is gentle, their potential power should not be underestimated. They are truly tools of transformation.

External Confounding Factors

There are however a few instances when flower remedies should not be used, or at least only with great caution, or an alternative should be employed. To return to the musical analogy: Of course there are external factors which may affect the performance of a symphony orchestra. Factors such as a power cut, a leaking roof, dry rot under the stage, or other problems can completely undermine or devastate the structure, negating the orchestra's best efforts. In the same way it is difficult for flower essences to do their job if external factors are strong enough to block or undermine them. Such factors might on occasion include geopathic stress, marked electromagnetic stress, chemical poisoning, nutritional deficiency and food intolerance.

Caroline was helped by Rescue Remedy, Mustard and Walnut after her husband's death. She passed through the grieving process successfully and healed her life. I had not seen her for a year, and then she arrived in my surgery distraught and 'in pieces'. She had gone back to smoking, had put on weight and generally let herself go. She had developed headaches and her energy level was low. On checking, it appeared that she needed an unusual combination of several flower remedies for her distressed state. Because the picture appeared unusual we looked into other factors. The problems had started just three months previously – soon after she had moved her bed. When she finally decided to move her bed back to where it had been before, all the problems resolved immediately. Subsequently a dowser checked the house. Along the wall where her head had been lying was a particularly bad line of geopathic stress.

Later Caroline told me how her husband had slept with his head in that line for two years before he died. The brain tumour that killed him became apparent a mere ten weeks before he died. Geopathic stress is now known to be an important factor in depleting the power of the immune system and the self-healing ability of the body.

Angela was 26, separated, and lived alone. Her commuting and work hours left little time for practising proper eating habits, so she lived on snacks, chocolate and junk food. Her mother had come to stay because she was worried about her daughter. Angela had begun to have paranoid thoughts about the people at work being out to harm her, and she was rather frightened even in the surgery. Although she was helped to regain her balance of mind by flower essences, they would have had little effect had she not taken vitamin supplements and started eating fresh food and a proper diet again. Within three weeks Angela was back to normal, and the planned psychiatric referral was cancelled.

Robert had tantrums at primary school that were disruptive to the class and to his own learning. Although Holly, Vine and Willow helped him a lot, his mother found that only by keeping him off certain foods did his behaviour remain balanced. These foods included oranges and some junk foods. Presumably citrus and food additives were the culprits.

Frances had become bossy and domineering, yet was not responding to Holly, Vine and Willow – which overlap with homeopathic Nux Vom. A few days later, she fell ill with a temperature, and became quiet and clingy. One single dose of the homeopathic remedy Pulsatilla made her better within minutes, and then she slept all afternoon. The next day, she was back to the bossy state, so I gave her a single dose of Nux Vom. It brought the same rapid resolution of her 'out-of-balance' state as had the Pulsatilla. This time the cure lasted and flower essences were not needed. So, on occasions, homeopathy or other treatments may be more appropriate than flower essences.

These four stories illustrate that, although flower remedies may seem to be indicated, there may be other factors which are more important to address first. In fact changing the other factors (as with geopathic stress) may be the only change needed.

The Placebo Response

The placebo response is a phenomenon well known to physicians and practitioners worldwide. It is the response that a person has to an inert (dummy) remedy or tablet. Medical trials determine the efficacy of a drug by comparing its effect against that of a placebo. Strangely the placebo is effective, say for pain relief, in 20 per cent of cases. In fact many doctors would like to be able to prescribe a placebo but for some reason they feel that it is unethical. The mechanism however is not fully understood.

Conventional doctors feel uncomfortable about not understanding the scientific mechanism of flower essences. However, they are happy to recognise them as non-threatening and useful, as these paragraphs, written by Dr Peter Glanvill, my partner in general medical practice, illustrate:

> It has long been my belief that as the practice of medicine becomes more focused and pharmacological treatments more precise, some individuals are in danger of being overtreated and of suffering from iatrogenic disease, that is illness caused by the treatment. Even fifty years ago the situation was very different – many diseases had no therapies associated with them. Consequently doctors relied on their personal abilities to ease their patients' distress, coupled with a number of preparations which often had little therapeutic benefit but were free from the risk of harming the patient.

> I have no doubt that there is a place in the medical practitioner's armament for 'benign' therapies which have no likelihood of causing iatrogenic disease. Such therapies would be suitable for self-limiting disorders and symptoms of transient mental turmoil.

> Although not comfortable with recommending therapies whose mode of action is inexplicable (or seems irrational) I am pragmatic enough to sanction their use wherever appropriate in conjunction with conventional medicine.

One simple explanation of the placebo effect runs as follows:
We all possess a strong inner healing power whose job it is to maintain
health and balance. For most of us this inner healer is not consciously
activated. When we take a substance or course of action that we think
will make us better, we are consciously activating the inner healer.
If we have great faith in our doctor, nurse, practitioner or our loved
carers then, again, we are consciously activating our inner healer.
If the people around us fear for our health and our life, we pick up
those vibes. Our inner healer is not only shut off, but the 'nocebo'
effect (opposite of the placebo) comes into play and we may become
more ill as a result.

An aboriginal medicine man knew all about this effect. When asked
what single thing he would suggest to improve Western treatment of
life-threatening illness, he replied that the medical system should 'stop
pointing the bone'. To point the bone at people is to suggest to them
that the spell of death is upon them.

We are often asked if the effect of flower remedies is merely a placebo.
For essences used on a child or an animal it is most unlikely that the
effect is a placebo. For adults choosing remedies for themselves
it is a different case. Although the remedies certainly have a powerful
effect, the placebo effect does exist, and for the following reason.

If you choose a remedy by reading the written word, or even mentally
identifying the correct essence (e.g. Holly for jealousy, revenge, envy,
suspicion and greed), you are in effect saying to your inner healer,
'I want to work on this bit of me.' Before you've even taken a single
drop of the essence your inner healer has been activated to work
on this aspect of you. And work it does, for you have consciously
activated the power of the inner healer. For most of us the inner healer
is only ticking over quietly, in neutral. A positive affirmation about
your health activates the healer powerfully, putting it in gear and
revving up the engine. The branch of science devoted to the
study of these effects is called psychoneuroimmunology.

The placebo mechanism is one of the most valuable yet least
understood tools that medicine can use. The powerful effect that
positive affirmations can have on health has not yet been harnessed

to our full benefit. With many essences, affirmations are supplied in order to amplify the healing potential of the remedy.

Psychoneuroimmunology is the modern scientific study of the effect of mind on matter. Specifically it looks at the effect of thoughts and emotions on the functioning of the immune system and health of the body. Modern research is now proving many of Dr Bach's observations and theories of health to be true.

Research over the next few years is likely to build up the scientific truth of the above mechanisms of action of flower remedies as a vital aspect of vibrational medicine. It will clarify many details which as yet are not fully understood. Such research is to be warmly welcomed! It will confirm scientifically what millions of people have learned by personal experience.

Chapter 5
How to Use Flower Essences

Bush Fuchsia

As we use flower essences, we develop increasing self-awareness and insight into what makes us tick. We begin to understand deeper motives and deeper aspects of our character. As the emotional broken glass of life gently dissolves, we can take a fresh look at life's journey and experiences. Flower essences support us during the processing and evaluation of these experiences. They dissolve the emotional sting of an acute situation, and allow us to heal recent or long-standing attitudes.

Flower essences are tools of transformation, catalysts for change that enable us to get in touch with our inner being and recognise the true nature of the issues, events and relationships of life. In a word, they help us heal ourselves.

Human Make-up

Each of us has his or her own particular make-up or personality type. This is partly personal, partly family-determined, partly genetic and partly racial. Each aspect is coloured by the tones and hues that comprise our personality – many different aspects and components of our essential nature, if you like. All of these factors are issues that face us during our journey through life, some major, some minor, some pressing and urgent, some subtle but crucial.

We each choose whether we wish to face these issues and transcend them, or ignore them. If we face them with optimism, listening to our intuitive guidance, the issue is processed painlessly. Experience is acquired and wisdom is gained. If we ignore the subtle hints, we are given further opportunities to learn. If we still persist in avoiding the issue, then the hints become blatantly obvious.

Imagine you are a workaholic. Nothing wrong with that. It is a conscious choice you have made. Deep within you there is a gentle feeling that all is not well. You ignore it, not recognising its origin.

Anyway, you're too busy. The subtle feeling becomes a little stronger, a vague feeling of discontent or that something is not quite right. Again you choose to ignore it. Next, the messages from the universe/ God-force/higher self (call it what you will) come via your work colleagues. 'Aren't you working rather hard? Don't you think you should take a day off?' You ignore it. 'You look as though you need a holiday,' is the next level of message.

The messages begin to be even more forceful. 'Are you sure the job's worth it?' After all, not a lot of people retire, give a sigh of relief and say 'I wish I'd spent more time at the office!' What happens next is a minor illness. You work through it. So you have to be sent another hint – influenza this time. If you still ignore the messages one of two things happen. If you're lucky, you get the sack. If you're unlucky, you get run over by a bus. Get the message now? Slow down! Be kind to yourself!

By the time the bus hits you, it is probably too late to use the flower remedies to help resolve the original issue. Events have taken hold of you! However, using the correct essences earlier in the process is a powerful way of catalysing change. The essences provide a supportive framework whilst the healing process takes place within your consciousness. This emotional healing process is our old friend from earlier in the book.

The Emotional Healing Process

- **Accept.** You first have to face the issue, no matter how uncomfortable.

- **Acknowledge.** The true nature of the issue becomes apparent.

- **Forgive.** Remember to do this in three ways: forgiveness of the other person, forgiveness of the event (or issue) and lastly forgiveness of yourself. Never forget to offer loving respect and forgiveness to yourself. Nearly all the world's human problems stem from failure at a deep level to love oneself. Why don't we love ourselves? Well, we simply forget to. And probably someone told us or implied that we weren't good/perfect/attractive/enough to be loved.

- **Release.** Are you quite sure you've finished the forgiveness? Then the releasing flows automatically into the next stage, being free to...

- **Move on.** Next challenge please! Or shall we have a little rest and just get on with life?

Passing through this sequence for each of life's events, challenges and issues allows us to gain experience and wisdom. 'Actually I'd rather earn a living. I'm too busy for all that emotional stuff,' you say. No problem. Just watch out for roaming buses – they may be out to get you!

Cynthia Kemp of the flower essence producers Desert Alchemy describes the concept of ancestral line contamination, where a trait or habit keeps recurring in a family, generation after generation. Often generations are skipped so that a trait such as addictive behaviour or alcoholism appears in a grandfather but not the parent. Her Ancestral Patterns Formula is helpful in these and other circumstances.

Probably all of us have to transcend some dysfunctional ancestral patterns as well as *miasms*. The concept of miasms was developed in homeopathy. Miasms are inherited stains which are not personal to the individual. The great homeopathic miasms are called Psoric, Syphilitic, Sycotic and Tuberculous. Pollution of the modern world has laid heavy metal, radiation and petrochemical miasms as additional loads to weaken our health and vitality. Flower essences can be very helpful in alleviating and dissolving these subtle miasms, especially in concert with homeopathy.

The Idea of Theme and Plot

Lila Devi of Masters Flower Essences has developed the idea of theme and plot essences. There are theme essences which help with your personality type. Can you guess mine? Have you noticed the excessive enthusiasm, the desire to convert everybody to my way of thinking, the rapid speech? My theme essence from the Bach system is Vervain. Vervain calms the busy, overactive mind. Complementing Vervain are the Master's Corn to restore mental vitality when I've burned up all my energy, and Verbena from Petite Fleur which is similar but subtly different to Vervain.

Theme essences are essences you return to time and again. They represent the major personality issues you are dealing with in this lifetime. My major personal issue is to learn patience and allow things to happen at their own pace, not mine. Have a think about what yours might be. Identifying your key issues leads you quickly to the appropriate essences. In fact, as you will remember from the discussion about placebo effect, merely identifying the issue starts the healing process – unless you block it with denial because it is too painful.

Plot essences help deal with specific issues which come up from time to time. Gerard was going through a negative phase when nothing seemed to be going right. All seemed failure, and he had lost his usual faith and conviction in his certainty of success. Gentian (Bach) might have helped him but Tomato (Masters) was exactly right. After six days he felt fully restored. Curiously, for two weeks before starting the remedy he had been craving tomato juice, an unusual choice for him. Perhaps his body knew what it needed and was dropping a hint?

Often a series of plots happen in turn, each supported by a different essence, as we learn about different issues and different facets of ourselves on our journey through life. Helper essences such as Walnut (Bach), which protects you in time of change, and Chestnut Bud which helps you gain insight and wisdom from life's events, are neither particularly theme or plot essences but are often useful.

The Confusion of Choice

But if there are 38 remedies in the Bach listings alone, how do you choose the correct ones? Does it matter if you don't? What happens if you choose the 'wrong' ones? How do you know which to take and when? And for how long? There are over 200 essences mentioned in this book and several thousand in the world. How can you choose the right ones? Isn't it all too confusing?

In this chapter all these questions will be answered. In the few years since I was given my first set of Flower Remedies I have had to answer them myself. At times I learned the hard way, but I hope to help you learn the easy way.

Intellectual and Intuitive Skills

Just as we have two sides to our brain and two ways of approaching life's problems, so there are also two approaches that can be used in choosing flower remedies. The mind has left-brain and right-brain talents. Both are important in leading a balanced and fulfilled life.

The left-brain, analytical, physical world skills are balanced by right-brain, intuitive, spiritual talents. Right-brain talents include knowing, healing, loving and creating. Left-brain talents include calculation, planning and rational approaches. Ideally, whatever our own personal make-up, our left-brain talents should be in balance with our right-brain ones.

Naturally people vary tremendously in their make-up. Some of us are more left-brain and prefer to take a rational approach; some of us are right-brain and automatically adopt an intuitive or instinctual approach. It used to be easy to make the generalisation that most men were more left-brain and most women more right-brain. This generalisation is no longer true, and anyway it's a very sexist remark. So I haven't made it!

It is often forgotten that we have all grown up in a left-brain society, whose leftward drift started with the beginnings of modern science in the Renaissance. Before that time the skilled right-brainers were the wise women and healers of society. But science and religion came to find the intuitive approach to knowledge a threat to the march of rational inquiry and the drift became a cruelly conscious step, with the persecution of hundreds of thousands of so-called witches and heretics. Sometimes mystics, alchemists and craftspeople, all of whom used their right-brain talents, might escape; sometimes they might be persecuted.

So today we all have a pronounced bias to the left-brain! We favour rational approaches above intuition. Authority figures (government, scientists, lawyers, doctors and so on) make, or presume to make, decisions on the basis of reason, not gut feeling. Or so they would claim publicly.

Yet many major scientific discoveries have been intuitive, leap-frogging a barrier of reason which allowed no further progress in a given direction. As children we all had substantially more right-brain awareness than we do as adults. No small child needs to be told how to pick something up or run. It does it perfectly happily and instinctively. A child exposed to foreign languages early enough will pick them up naturally – the spoken language (right-brain) that is, not the grammar (left-brain). But if you saw fairies or 'imaginary' friends as a three-year-old, you had probably lost that talent by the age of five. It was shut down by the cold climate of peers or adults who disapproved, didn't believe in, or rubbished, your abilities.

Instead we all learned our left-brain skills in what society considered to be important, e.g. maths, grammar and other intellectual skills. Of course art, music and flower-arranging exercise the creative intuitive faculty, but only to a limited degree when compared to the phenomenal potential available. A recent experiment on a class of primary school children showed all 35 to be able to dowse (a highly developed right-brain skill).

Choosing Essences Intellectually

The leaflets on the 38 Bach remedies give brief descriptions of 38 different states of mind. When I first read the cameos I quickly chose a mere 32, discarding only six! Two days later I narrowed my choice to 16, but it took considerable soul-searching to get down to 12!

Actually it is uncommon in practice to benefit from more than six Bach remedies at any particular time.

This experience showed me the difficulty of choosing for myself, at least at the beginning. To choose wisely you need insight into your own personality, your needs, your hopes and your fears. It is actually very difficult to appreciate your own need for Holly (jealousy, envy, revenge, suspicion and greed), Vine (always right, never need to argue, always know best and tell you they do), Impatiens (impatience and irritability), and Willow (bitterness and resentment). On the other hand it's surprising how easy it is to know when a friend, partner or relative needs any of these four.

But the process of choosing accurately for yourself does have its reward, in terms of the insight it brings into your own personality. This insight catalyses growth and change, a process which the essences help initiate and support. The intellectual approach helps consolidate the benefits of insight and wisdom that are gained by observing the process of personal change and growth.

One of the problems for me was that the original literature, such as Dr Bach's *The Twelve Healers*, tends to give the most negative and extreme picture about a remedy. Actually the positive quality brought by taking the essence is just as important in choosing wisely. After all, we'd all like more of the quality of vitality, sound judgement and pleasure in living. But not many of us equate this with the remedy Pine if we read 'guilt, self-blame and self-reproach'.

It certainly isn't easy to detect your own need for Holly (hatred) or Willow (bitterness), yet some practitioners usually give one or other of these in the first treatment bottle. These two remedies address two of the most important aspects that need healing before any other problems can be addressed, yet recognising the speck in someone else's eye is always far easier than spotting the plank in your own!

Reading the positive aspects of a remedy is just as important as reading the negative. Sometimes our friends can help. They can generally see our imperfections as easily as we can find theirs. Of course if they are too closely related they may be emotionally involved in the problem and so unable to give unbiased help.

Top: *Orange Pincushion (South African Crisis Essence)*

Bottom left: *Wild Iris (South African Creativity Essence)*

Bottom right: *Strelitzia (South African Creativity and Crisis Essences)*

Top: *Chinkerinchee (South African Substance Abuse Essence)*

Bottom: *Dune Calendula (South African Adolescent, Menopause, Study and Substance Abuse Essences)*

Dr Bach advised the user to pay particular attention to one's outlook on life. He identified twelve key personality traits and found remedies for each of these.

- Weakness: Centaury

- Terror: Rock Rose

- Fear: Mimulus

- Mental torture: Agrimony

- Indecision: Scleranthus

- Indifference: Clematis

- Fussiness: Chicory

- Self-distrust: Cerato

- Discouragement: Gentian

- Over-enthusiasm: Vervain

- Impatience: Impatiens

- Aloofness: Water Violet

Later he categorised emotions into seven main groups, each with several different facets: Fear; Loneliness; Insufficient interest in present circumstances; Despondency or despair; Uncertainty; Over-sensitivity to influences and ideas; Over-care for the welfare of others.

One useful starting point is to write your symptoms on a sheet of paper, particularly the mental and emotional ones. Write down also your reactions to any recent stresses or challenges. Add any major life events, sadnesses, problems or issues.

Try and draw out some themes from these and relate them to one or more of the seven categories Dr Bach described, if it is to be Bach Remedies you choose from. Choose at most six or seven essences, then try and narrow down your choice further. What you are left with are the remedies to use at present. The tighter you are able to make your choice, the more you benefit from the insight you gain from being critical in your choosing. In other words, a critical self-analysis has its own benefits – bringing insight into your own personality and consequent emotional challenges.

Bach Remedies are widely available, but other ranges, including the Masters and the Australian Bush, are particularly suited to the beginner as well, if these are what you have available. There is certainly great merit in buying a whole set if you can afford it. All the ranges described in the next chapter have essences to help solve the common problems we all share. If you cannot afford a whole set, choose the one that most fits your needs and your pocket.

Feel free to use remedies from any of the systems mentioned in this book if they are appropriate. You can choose more remedies than seven, but often the descriptions may appear similar for different essences, though they might have different characters. At this point you can either call in a skilled counsellor and essence practitioner, or you can realise an important new truth namely, that there can be pitfalls in the process of taking a history, identifying a need and selecting the correct remedies.

There are actually a number of essences from which everybody benefits if taken in a 4-6 week course:

- Star of Bethlehem for long slow shock over the years or in childhood

- Holly to bring out love

- Mustard, Walnut and Willow to process any past traumatic or sad events – we all have them! Adding Sturt Desert Pea to these three makes a very powerful combination

- Pine is for the shoulds and shouldn'ts of life that weigh heavily on our shoulders.

In a later chapter you will find some broad hints and guidelines to get you started with a combination of essences for particular problems. Also, Chapter 2 has some helpful guidance.

Intellectual versus Intuitive Approach

Words are often inadequate to describe the difference of timbre, pitch and harmonic between essences which may have similar descriptions but differing depths and emphasis of action. In Britain we have a handful of words that describe snow – but Eskimos are said to have over thirty.

Does it matter, as long as the words fit? At a basic level of treatment probably not. The emergency combinations in Rescue Remedy, Five Flower Remedy, Emergency Essence, Crisis Combination, Terra and all the other systems broadly work for everybody with similarly acute emotional trauma. However, once you move more deeply into the nuances of treatment, it does start to matter.

You can get a long way in emotional healing with the remedies of one producer or system, but there comes a time when you reach the buffers. And if you happen to have several hundred essences to choose from, how can you do that accurately and swiftly? You probably can't do so on a purely intellectual level.

The intellectual approach can take you a long way on the journey of healing, especially as you gain familiarity and experience with your essences. An experienced practitioner with counselling skills can probably take you further again. But sooner or later you reach the point where you know there is still work that needs to be done but just can't figure out what it is or how to go about it.

An obvious example is in relation to unresolved emotions from early childhood. These are notoriously difficult to ferret out, even if you know they are there. And what if they are long-forgotten, or suppressed in the unconscious because they are too painful to remember? May I give you a personal story?

Despite having three daughters who are keen and confident swimmers, until recently I would always avoid a family swim and make excuses, though I didn't know why. If pushed, I would join the swim, but grudgingly. Taking Larch transformed my attitude to

LAZY PERSON'S GUIDE TO EMOTIONAL HEALING

that of a keen swimmer who would take myself off to the pool alone – something unheard of in the family. Larch catalysed the change, which I was then able to see stemmed from a blockage of confidence which started at the age of eight, when I had learned to swim at boarding school under duress, unhappy and unconfident in a cold outdoor pool. That blockage had coloured my attitude to swimming at a subconscious level for 30 years until dissolved by a few weeks' treatment with Larch.

One of the most rewarding moments I have seen with flower essences was this one:

Sarah is 39. She had always appeared sad and edgy, unsure of herself. Then one day, glowing with confidence, she breezed into the surgery in a state of self-assuredness I had never seen before. We dealt with her presenting problem. Intrigued, I asked why she felt different. Sarah told me that she had taken the Australian Sexuality Essence for two months. She was thrilled because she could now cuddle and hug her children, her mother and other relatives. This had been impossible before. Sarah, like many women, had suffered sexual abuse in her childhood. Despite counselling, she had not felt good about herself and her own sexuality. She was overjoyed to share the change with me, and hoped that many other women might also benefit. Certainly, to take a course of Relationship Essence, followed by Sexuality Essence, can have profound effects on the psyche. For Sarah, just the one helped enormously.

As we heard from Pamela in Chapter 4, taking certain essences for a period of time can actually help reveal long-forgotten memories and allow them to be processed and healed. But to do this just in hope of hitting the right combination for the right length of time in the right sequence is hit-and-miss, to say the least. Practitioners using the intellectual/counselling approach know that when a course of one essence combination has been taken, then more often than not different issues surface and need to be dealt with. It's a bit like peeling away the skins of an onion – there's always another layer!

The intellectual reasoning method of choice can take you a long way and is the method that should be mastered before adopting the complementary intuitive approach. A sound knowledge of structure and procedure is essential. Such knowledge can avoid some elementary mistakes. However, the intellect cannot always clearly perceive the nature of the journey.

Imagine starting a journey without a map or a clear idea of destination. The weather is cold and foggy, the ground underfoot uneven and boggy. The journey soon becomes chaotic. One step forward, one to the side, two back, without any certainty of whether or not the direction is correct. If you were to travel in this way you would never be sure whether you were facing north, south, east or west.

Now imagine that not only is the destination unclear and no map is available, but also that you are sitting, blindfolded, on a horse. What is worse, nobody told you it was a horse, nor have you ever learned to ride. A recipe for disaster? Not exactly, but there are painful parallels to be drawn with the journey we call life. The majority of us have no clear view of the destination. We take one step forward, one back, two sideways. If we reach any destination, let alone the correct one, it is likely to be more by luck than by good judgement.

In childhood we all put on the blindfolds and denied ourselves the riding lessons. We ignored the development of our intuitive right-brain skills and concentrated on left-brain reasoning and physical world skills. We did this because everybody else did it and none of us knew any different.

Young children have a great ability to day-dream. This is a right-brain activity that acts to refresh them. As adults we tend to shirk this activity, 'because we are too busy'. The result is that we deny ourselves valuable skills to help us with life's problems and challenges. How often have we tussled with a problem to distraction, seeing no rational solution? Then we relax, put the problem aside and after a little while the answer just pops into our minds!

It seems that, sometimes, the harder we concentrate on the rational-analytical approach to a problem, the further we drive the solution away. If we allow our intuition or gut feelings to help us with the answer and then use the reasoning intellect to guide us safely to the known destination, driving carefully, stopping at red lights, and so on, then the journey will go smoothly. Too intuitive an approach results in a vague disconnected feeling and the temptation to ignore cosmically unimportant elements such as traffic lights and speed limits. Too rigid an intellectual stance results in a pedantic, excessively rigid journey where everything is done by the rule book, but the traffic jam wins out, because the little inner voice saying 'Go this way today for a change' was ignored.

The coach-and-horses is a famous analogy from the philosopher Gurdjieff. The coach is the physical body, the horses the emotions, the coachman the intellect and the person inside is the intuitive driving force or soul. All facets need to be in balance for the journey to go smoothly.

Permit me a personal example. At school I studied Greek, Latin, Ancient History and Economics. These are not the usual entry subjects for Medical School! Fortunately, Guy's Hospital ran a preliminary year of appropriate sciences. Physics practicals were designed to last from 2pm to 5pm on a Tuesday. Out of a class of twenty, four of us had a little familiarity with physics, or so we liked to think. We felt this because usually we had worked out the answer by 2.10pm and, allowing some 'errors' in the working, still managed to leave by the indecently early time of 2.25pm at the latest.

> Looking back now, I am certain that what really happened was that we read the question, intuited the answer using right-brain skills and then used the left-brain counterpart to get from A to B with the minimum of effort. Naturally this approach freed up a lot of time and energy for the more pressing engagements that medical students seem to acquire!

In a similar way a homing pigeon doesn't need to learn where to fly. It just does it. And have you ever watched a flock of a thousand starlings wheeling around at dusk and wondered how they don't all bump into each other? Do they have to think about it?

Whether you choose intellectually or intuitively, I urge you to use both faculties to check your answers. If well-chosen remedies don't 'feel right' there may be a good reason. If intuited remedies do not fit with the known facts, then either there is something going on that you haven't considererd, or your intuition is off-beam, e.g. you are overtired, ignoring hunger, or responding to other needs more pressing than looking at remedies.

Choosing Intuitively

Here we shall look at four ways of choosing flower essences intuitively: scanning, dowsing, kinesiology, and flower cards. The first relies on picking up subtle hints from your thoughts; the next two give precise visible indications. One more advanced technique, Baihui diagnosis, is described in *Australian Flower Essences for the 21st Century.*

Scanning

Scanning is the simplest method of intuitive diagnosis. It involves just quickly reading through a list of essences and picking the first ones that spring to mind or catch your attention. It is surprising how often this approach yields accurate results when the remedy descriptions are checked by the person to whom they apply.

Sometimes reading the names of the essences is sufficient, though, more often, scanning the descriptions yields results. Your abilities in diagnosis and remedy choice by scanning depend very much on natural flair, experience, and how 'tuned in' (attuned) you are at the time.

Dowsing

Dowsing for water or minerals is an ancient art, used worldwide throughout time. Armies and those living in tropical countries and elsewhere have used the technique to find a safe water supply. Col Kenneth Merrylees OBE of the British Army worked during the Second World War as a bomb disposal expert, when he used his dowsing skills to find deep, unexploded, delayed-action bombs. One he successfully discovered had burrowed under the swimming pool at Buckingham Palace. His skill in the Middle East and India at finding water in barren places earned him the title 'God of the water'.

> I am not exceptional among 'sensitives' in that I am, after a short time, acutely uncomfortable if I stay on the lines of a fair-sized flow, and I know from experience it's impossible for me to sleep over one. I found it impossible to accept a purely physical explanation of the dowser's ability. I am forced therefore to look beyond the limitations of orthodox physics and the five senses.

Col Merrylees dismissed the idea that a dowser's skills are supernatural, though he maintained there is a connection made by the dowser's mind with a source of knowledge beyond all physical limits. Success in dowsing, he felt, requires effort, study and practice, and dowsing is sometimes discredited because dowsers make avoidable mistakes.

Col Merrylees was Chairman of the British Society of Dowsers. More recently Dr Arthur Bailey, former senior lecturer in Electronics and Electrical Engineering at the University of Bradford, has been President. I encountered the Bailey essences after working with the Bach remedies. I wrote asking Dr Bailey to dowse for me and was amazed at the accuracy of his description. I must add that we did not know each other at that time.

Having someone you have never met dowse an accurate prescription for you is a little like having someone walk over your grave. It shakes you. Or rather, it threatens your highly cherished emotionally-held beliefs about the nature of the universe.

You have a number of options at this point. You can either deny what has happened, ignore it, dismiss it as a fluke or a coincidence, throw a tantrum, or consign the episode to a box labelled 'Paranormal' to be conveniently ignored. This may explain why a respected colleague once called me a charlatan, a dangerous person. After all, if someone challenges a belief that is emotionally dear, you can easily get angry, rather than ask yourself whether, perhaps, the earth does actually go round the sun, despite all you have been taught. People have been excommunicated or executed for less! By the way, someone once told me that 'Coincidence is God's way of remaining anonymous!'

Or, faced with something that has challenged your belief system or paradigm, you can approach it in an honest, inquiring frame of mind. I'm not saying that the first course of action is wrong, only that if you have a strong emotional reaction to something challenging, you are well advised to ask where this strong reaction is coming from.

Is it from your inner wisdom, a place of comfortable security and knowing? Or is it from the ego, that vulnerable part of us that craves security and can only obtain it by flexing the 'I'm better than you/you're different to me' muscles – those muscles that have to be continually flexed to maintain a confident posture, whilst all the time the ego suffers fear, a fear built on ignorance.

Facing these options, though I didn't understand them at the time, I chose to just take Dr Bailey's dowsed remedies. Funnily enough, they were a combination which opened up my intuition and enabled me to think laterally. Soon after this I also learned to dowse!

Learning to Dowse

Dowsing is merely a means of accessing intuition. It involves using an external indicator such as a hazel twig (hazel is flexible), a pair of rods or a pendulum to indicate a response to a question. Essentially the only possible answers are *Yes*, *No* or *Maybe*.

Maybe, otherwise known by the technical name of **!!???**, happens when the answer is neither *Yes* nor *No.* It can also indicate an inappropriate question, or an area about which you are not permitted to ask, for example, 'Is this horse to be the winner of the Grand National?' Such a question is for personal gain and is an abuse of the skill.

Using your intuition, with or without dowsing, seems to tap into something universal, perhaps a universal web of consciousness. From this higher perspective questions that come from the ego (such as racing results with an aim for personal gain) do not appear to wish for answers that are in accordance with the highest good of all living things. Therefore an ego-based question will attract an ego-based answer. You will probably lose the stake on your horse too!

One other point – any emotional investment in the result can unduly influence the answer. This is particularly true if you are choosing remedies for somebody else. Also, if when you are dowsing, others are close by you, it is possible for them to influence the results if they are projecting strong feelings or thoughts towards you. So make sure you are emotionally balanced and free of anticipations and prejudgments when you dowse for essences.

Dowsing needs very accurate, well-formulated questions in order to avoid woolly or confused answers. In fact, dowsing with a pendulum is a very left-brain way of accessing a right-brain skill. Of course, it's not the pendulum that gives the answer. A pendulum is just an external indicator of how your body sub-consciously responds to a question. Examine your own feelings to a statement, perhaps 'I love you'. Are you tense, or relaxed? Now see how you feel to a statement that says the opposite. Relaxed, or perhaps a little tense? What a swinging pendulum does is to pick up the minute differences in tension in your body that relate to either positive (relaxing) or negative (tensioning) feelings.

Please note that a pendulum or any other intuitive tool should only ever be used with an honest, true and high motive. Use of intuition should come from the heart without thought of personal gain. When the intention is to use an intuitive tool for the highest good, only good can occur.

Getting Started

Shall we try it together? Your pendulum needs be no more hi-tech than a washer on the end of a piece of string. As long as the weight is sufficiently heavy to hold the string taut, your pendulum will work. Try different weights and lengths of string so that the pendulum swings nicely. When you are ready, we'll begin.

Time to relax and allow yourself to play gently. Hold the string between finger and thumb with your arm just out-stretched. Relax! It's not an exam. Nobody's watching! If you hold yourself too tense, nothing will happen.

Just allow your arm to relax. The pendulum may start to swing gently. The shorter the string, the faster the oscillations. To start with, a string of about 15cm or six inches is sufficient. If you can feel a gentle swing, that's good. If not, don't worry. Once you feel relaxed and comfortable say out loud or to yourself: 'Please show me a Yes.'

The pendulum will now adopt a definite direction to its swing. It differs from person to person. For me, a Yes is a clockwise swing, though for others it could be a straight swing towards and away from you. But whatever is right for you is just fine. Now stop the swing and let's start again. It can take a minute or two to get your very first swing.

'Now, please show me a No.' Be patient. Allow the pendulum to start swinging again. This time the swing is in a different direction. For me a No is backwards and forwards, or for others it could be a sideways or anti-clockwise swing.

Don't worry if this doesn't work for you the first time. It didn't for me. Just allow yourself to practise, and try and daydream during your practice. The relaxed state of mind will help you. Sometimes allowing a practised dowser to hold your arm when first starting can help you progress quickly, but many people manage alone.

If you find getting a Yes or No difficult as a concept, the following technique may help. Find a battery, perhaps a torch battery. Dowse over the + or positive end, asking 'Please show me a Yes'. Now repeat the process at the other end of the battery, the − or negative No end. Once you have differentiated between Yes and No you are in a position to ask questions. Such questions must be precise and unambiguous, that is, only capable of a Yes or No answer. A vague question will attract a vague answer. Computers can only work on Yes and No – on or off – and asking questions with a pendulum shares this characteristic.

There is a set routine which is worth using in dowsing. It runs as follows: Settle yourself and make sure you are comfortable. Sit, or stand, which ever you feel is best. Uncross legs and arms (crossed arms and legs can alter the result). Relax your arm and let your pendulum hang down. Follow this process:

• Please show me a Yes.

• Please show me a No.

• Am I fit to dowse? (You may be too tired or wound up to do so)

• May we talk about (name the subject in mind)?

If the answer to the third question is No then the number you are dialling is otherwise engaged. Please try again later! If the answer to the fourth question is No, then the number you are dialling is unobtainable at present. Sorry, please try another line!

Assuming all is well, you can now ask some questions. Let's suppose you wish to choose remedies for yourself. Make sure the particular issue is clearly in your mind. Make sure your whole range of remedies is in front of you. Now proceed as follows: Are there any flower essences amongst these in front of me that will help me with this issue/help me generally/help my emotional health? (Choose your question.)

Use the most appropriate formula, or make up your own. Note that you have specified the essences in front of you. Otherwise you would end up with some confusing answers. Assuming the answer is Yes, the next step is to choose the appropriate ones. It is helpful at this point to hold in your mind the intention that you wish to choose a balanced combination of essences.

You could now ask which essences to use by hanging the pendulum over, pointing to, or touching each bottle in turn and asking if this one is appropriate. If you only have ten this is a perfectly good method. If you are choosing from the whole Bach set (38) or from, say, Bailey, Bloesem, Korte, Australian Bush, Masters, Petite Fleur and Desert Alchemy as well, there are short cuts. Since this list includes several hundred essences, a short cut will save you time.

Some people next ask for the total number of essences they will be combining in their treatment bottles. 'Does the most appropriate balanced combination for me contain a single essence? Two only? Three only? Four only?' Note that if you ask 'one' rather than 'one only' you will get a Yes whether the true answer is one, two or six. Note that the answers can only be Yes or No, so make sure the question is precise and unambiguous!

Then ask about each box in turn. Are any of the essences I seek in this box?' (Do not ask 'Are there any essences in this box?' The answer of course is Yes unless the box is empty!) Do you see how important the precision of the questions is? If you get a No answer to a box, you have saved checking each individual essence in that box. See the short cut? If you get a Yes, then take each rank or column separately: 'Are any of the essences I seek in this rank/column?' You should have only four or five to choose from. If you have eight or ten, mentally divide the box in half and ask, 'Are any of the essences I seek to the left of halfway?' and then continue your process of elimination.

Having chosen your combination, you are ready to make up a treatment bottle. We'll come to treatment bottles a little later. Dowsing enables you to ask how many drops of each different essence to put into your treatment bottle. You can also ask how many drops to put under your tongue, and how frequently.

Sometimes answers come up in your dowsing that may at first appear incorrect. What is happening here is that you may be uncovering a deep need that is not obvious to your conscious state. It may be from the past, it may apply to a particular unresolved issue, or it may even not be particularly personal, but relate to current issues in the world psyche. For example, many people are helped at present by Cerato, Chicory, Mustard and Walnut. These essences are generic essences to help issues that the whole human race is facing, but they may also apply personally. You only have to listen to the news to recognise the generic need for Mustard and Walnut! Even deeper, every one of us carries archetypal memories deep within, which may also be healed and resolved by appropriate use of essences.

Advanced Dowsing

Some people have the skill of 'list dowsing'. It involves choosing remedies by name from a list. This is helpful when you do not have the essence actually in front of you. It is a skill that has to be practised in order to develop it.

Back to Col Merrylees, the expert dowser who could detect unexploded bombs and water: 'I do not dowse to find minerals, missing people or lost objects nor do I detect diseases, but I am always learning.' He felt that different people have differing abilities to dowse and differing areas of expertise. Personally I find at present that I can work intuitively with considerable accuracy on flower essences but that map dowsing or finding lost objects are not my particular fields. They may however, with practice, be yours!

The answers you get by dowsing seem to be limited in scope, but only by the scope of your questioning. Some time ago I thought I had cleared and healed everything in myself for the time being and then I found all sorts of strange emotions coming up to the surface including some spitefulness (Holly) and resentment (Willow). Trying to find out where it was coming from was fun!

Eventually I came up with a number of different aspects of myself to ask about, on the basis that the more precise the questioning, the higher the quality of answers. In fact, in life, it appears that once you have correctly formulated the question, the answer becomes obvious. The different aspects you could ask for include:

- Your highest good
- Physical level
- Emotional level
- Mental level

- Etheric level

- Personality

- Past episodes of sadness – there can be several, each needing separate identification

- Past generally – for example a long, slow shock

- Future issues whose seeds are coming to the surface

- For your masculine aspects

- For your feminine aspects

- Is there one single core issue?

- Are you lost yet ??? !!!

You really don't have to go so deep. It is quite sufficient to ask for the most appropriate combination for the present. But it is important to know about these aspects, even if you never need to use them.

Sometimes it is useful to ask, on a scale of nought to ten, how important this issue is, or how much it has been resolved already. Ten would represent unresolved; nought, fully resolved; one, 90 percent resolved, and so on. For example, you might carry a sadness from the loss of a grandparent to be resolved using Mustard and Walnut, which scored 2 intuitively. This would mean that the issue is nearly fully resolved, but could do with just a little more healing.

When you have completed your intuitive selection, do read about each essence, particularly the positive aspects of the remedy picture. Doing this is a valuable way to gain self-knowledge and insight.

Kinesiology

Kinesiology has many facets, but fortunately only two are used in basic essence testing. Both seek the body's response, like dowsing to a Yes or No question.

The first method involves finger circuit testing. Create a circuit by holding together the tips of thumb and little finger. If this feels awkward use thumb and index finger. If you are right-handed, make the circuit with your left hand, or vice-versa.

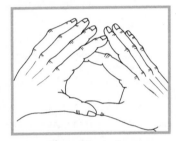

Finger Circuit Closed   *Finger Circuit Open*

You have just made an electrical circuit. You can check it for positive Yes and negative No responses like this: Using the thumb and index finger of your other hand, like opening a pair of scissors, try and force the circuit open. Ask 'Please show me a Yes' as you do it. Now compare your response to a No. The two should be different. As with dowsing, take care not to cross your legs. Most people's Yes is when the circuit opens easily (the body feels relaxed), and their No is when the circuit cannot be forced open. Some people have the opposite. Just like dowsing, there is also a Maybe, which generally appears as a No-Yes.

The second method involves applying light downwards pressure to an outstretched arm. The arm is held horizontally out from the body, and light pressure from another person as a question is asked will produce a response. The response is either to remain strong, with the arm unmoved by the pressure, or to become weak, in which case the arm is unable to resist the other person's light pressure. In this method the novice can weaken very quickly, and thus obtain misleading results. If you wish to learn this method, ask the help of a kinesiologist.

Flower Cards

Some producers have made sets of photographic cards of the flowers corresponding to the essences. By looking through a pack, many people will find themselves drawn to one or more particular pictures. There appears to be a resonance, or the picture has 'good vibes'. Some pictures may make you feel uncomfortable – this may hint at issues which you would rather not confront. Essences chosen by this method often have particularly deep resonance with an aspect needing healing that is difficult to discover in other ways.

Having made your choice intuitively, read up the descriptions of each essence and assess them honestly. The process of assessing gives valuable insights and can help you identify areas of your life you feel reluctant to look at. The assessment helps to clarify issues and avoid pitfalls. Here is an interesting pitfall:

> Louise chose four Bailey essences intuitively one afternoon. When she read about them, she exclaimed, 'These aren't for me. They're for my husband!' As we talked, it became clear that he had been very much on her mind for the previous few days, and so subconsciously she had chosen remedies for this state of mind, not for hers personally! The same could have happened if she were projecting her emotions on to him.

Now you are ready to make up a balanced combination for yourself in a treatment bottle.

Treatment Bottles

Use a clean 30ml dropper bottle, obtainable from most pharmacies. Fill it with spring (not boiled) water, adding 2-3ml of brandy or vodka. The spirit is to lengthen the shelf life of the bottle to four weeks or so. If you are intolerant to alcohol, use a mixture of spring water and ¼ cider vinegar or vegetable glycerine. Spring water with no additives will keep in the refrigerator for a week at maximum.

Add your chosen combination of essences, using three drops of each. If you are dowsing, check the exact number of drops to use. Take care not to touch the dropper from the stock bottle on your treatment bottle, as the stock bottle needs to be kept pure. When you have put all your remedies into the treatment bottle, replace the top. The bottle is nearly ready to use, but the essences have now been diluted from stock strength and combined.

In theory there are no problems from this, but in practice there is one very important thing you can do to make the treatment bottle balanced and working at full potency: Bless the bottle. Yes, that's right, *bless it!* If reading this fills you with alarm, don't worry! Performing this simple step has a hugely favourable placebo effect! Hold the bottle between your cupped hands, be still and, in whatever way you feel appropriate according to your beliefs and religious persuasion, ask something like this: 'May this treatment bottle work as a balanced combination at full potency for my highest good.' Then give thanks if you wish.

Take care that your blessing of the bottle, for that is what it is, is made from the heart as an expression of unconditional love. It is inappropriate to use willpower to force the issue. To inflict a strong will inevitably involves the ego and will bring unlooked-for problems.

When blessing the bottle some people feel a tingle in their hands. This is an example of the activation of a healing power. We all have this healing ability to a greater or lesser extent. Do not worry if you don't feel this. What you have done is powerful enough anyway. Whatever else is happening, you are making a very powerful positive affirmation about your intentions. If this doesn't start your inner healer working, the essence combination certainly will!

The treatment bottle is now ready. Take care not to touch the dropper with your tongue, for this will contaminate the bottle and bacteria may spoil it. Place three drops carefully on to your tongue four to six times daily, or otherwise as guided by your own intuition. If you keep the bottle with you, in your pocket or handbag, it will be available whenever you feel prompted to take it.

Some people choose to take essences direct from the stock bottle. Essences can also be sprayed around the body using a mister, put into the bath or used in other creative ways such as placing them on chakras or acupressure points. Should you wish to give someone an Emergency Essence, for instance, but not put alcohol on to their tongue, the front or palmar surface of the wrist has several meridians of energy which will pick up the vibration of the remedy and take it into the body. The Large Intestine Four point, called the Great Reliever, between the thumb and index finger, is another useful point of application.

As you take the remedy, don't be surprised if nothing appears to happen at first. Very often when you first use essences it may take a few days to notice an effect. Actually, your friends may notice a difference before you do. Over time the issues for which you chose your combination will surface and appear in a different, more positive light, allowing you to gain experience and wisdom from them as you release any emotional sting they hold for you.

Sometimes there may be a need to re-evaluate the situation after a few days if you find new issues or emotions emerging. This is not uncommon and shows that the remedies are working. At that point you may need to add some other remedies to your combination.

In homeopathy an aggravation or 'healing crisis' can occur. This is when the symptoms temporarily worsen before improving, and it may be a sign that the chosen agent is a good frequency match, but possibly at a sub-optimal potency. In flower essence therapy, aggravations are rare as long as there is no potentisation by serial succussion, as in homeopathy, and even then they are uncommon. This method of preparation was not advised by Dr Bach. In fact it was his search for a means of avoiding such aggravations that led him to his method of preparation of flower remedies.

Aggravations or healing crises can occur in flower remedy therapy, even if rarely. If you should get one, it may be because the emotion that it is treating is strongly held within you, and perhaps it was buried because it was too painful to process at the time. If this is the case, then supportive methods can help.

The healing crisis may bring deep insights and understanding as a result. To get through it, however, some support may be helpful.

Suggestions include grounding the feelings by writing them down on paper to release them, then burning the paper; taking your remedy less frequently for a while; using a supporting remedy such as Walnut (Bach); having help and sympathy from a friend; taking a walk in nature, or other helpful means.

At any stressful time the simple technique of centering yourself by breathing slowly and deeply from your Hara or balance point, low down in your abdomen, is an incredibly powerful one. It is even more calming if you put the tip of your tongue behind your top teeth on the roof of your mouth.

Over a few days and weeks, as you take flower essences, you will notice their incredibly powerful yet gentle action working as tools of transformation and as catalysts for change. To help develop self-knowledge and awareness as you heal it is useful to keep a diary or journal of any feelings and memories which surface.

It is worth remembering that we all carry several layers of emotional imbalance. It is not uncommon for an appropriate first essence combination to unmask another layer, often a sadness one, which immediately deserves a different combination such as the Bereavement Mix or the Blues Mix.

Chapter 6
Combination Essences

Herb Paris

This chapter reviews combination essences as supplied by the world's major makers, and gives some suggestions of combinations that you might wish to make up yourself from widely available essences.

Descriptions are generally those of the maker or originator, enhanced by knowledge gained from widespread use of an essence.

When you decide to look further into essences, the choice can become bewildering. Most flower remedies are known by the name of the relevant flower, which means learning the properties of each essence, as well as determining what state of mind you wish to treat. Some producers have created combination sets in the way that Dr Bach created Rescue Remedy. The advantage of this is that it helps you choose in one step, not two.

We are normally introduced to flower essences through Rescue Remedy, Five Flower Remedy, or one of the other trauma and shock remedies. These are all combination remedies. Combinations are particularly useful – they do what their names suggest, and are specially formulated by the essence maker to do just that. The use of combination remedies helps us gain familiarity in choosing flower essences. It is difficult to guess what Honeysuckle, Holly and Purple Flag Flower do, but relatively easy to interpret combinations such as Woman-essence, Inner Child and Tranquillity.

Is it necessary to use only essences from your own country? The answer is definitely no, for the essences have global application. Wherever we live, as members of the human race we all share similar colours of emotion. All of us can be helped by essences from different parts of the world, just as we can all appreciate music from different times and different places.

Rescue/Crisis/Emergency Essences from around the world

Rescue Remedy (Nelson's), **Five Flower Essence** (Healing Herbs), **Recovery Essence** (Ainsworth's), **Emergency Essence** (Crystal Herbs and Sun Essences), **RQ, RQ6, RQ7** (Milagra), **Situations de Crise** (Deva). The classic combination, formulated by Dr Bach, consists of Cherry Plum, Clematis, Impatiens, Rock Rose and Star of Bethlehem. Some add Larimar, Self Heal or Lotus to enhance the effect. Rescue Remedy helps dissolve the emotional effects of shock, fear, accidents and emergencies, restoring calm and stability.

Clematis

Emergency Essence (Australian Bush). Contains Crowea, Fringed Violet, Grey Spider Flower, Sundew and Waratah. Again, this helps ease distress, fear and panic, bringing calm and stability.

Crisis Desert Emergency Formulation (Desert Alchemy). Contains Aloe, Cliff Fendlerbush, Desert Holly, Klein's Pencil Cholla Cactus and Purple Aster. Helps one stay calm in danger and in emergency situations.

Crisis Remedy (South African). Contains Bacometra, Disa, Felicia, Flowering Quince, Orange Pincushion, Red Camellia and Strelitzia. Works to bring calm in situations of shock, panic, fear and anxiety.

First Aid (Bailey). Comprising Star of Bethlehem, Ivy and Scabious, this remedy brings calm and stability whilst dissolving emotional shock.

Trauma Shock (Harebell). Contains Bluebell, Chamomile, Comfrey and Red Clover. Particularly helpful after physical injury or operations.

Pacific Balancer (Pacific Essences). A great stabiliser and regenerator. Useful in any case of psychic, emotional or physical overload.

First Aid (Findhorn). Contains Scottish Primrose, Thistle, Bell Heather and Daisy.

Pear (Masters). Although a single essence, this particular remedy is a powerful stabiliser in times of shock. It brings peacefulness and a dynamic yet relaxed state of mind.

Wildflower Relief Elixir (Australian Living). For shock and distress.

Terra (Bloesem). Comprises Angelica, Clematis, Mycena, Rode Bosvogeltje Orchid and Yellow Star Tulip. Acts as a first-aid remedy in situations of tension, shock and trauma.

Combinations to make up yourself

These are not sold as made-up combinations, but are tried and tested and can easily be put together.

BACH

Relationship Mix. Beech, Chicory, Gentian, Heather, Holly, Impatiens, Mustard, Pine, Red Chestnut, Sweet Chestnut, Vine, Walnut, Willow. For clear honest communication and forgiveness.

Bitch Mix (Anger and Irritation). Beech, Cherry Plum, Holly, Impatiens, Pine, Vine and Willow. For irritability both premenstrually and for any wish to dominate or control, or for jealousy, negativity and bitterness or resentment.

Confidence Mix. Agrimony, Centaury, Chestnut Bud, Gentian, Larch, Pine, Sweet Chestnut, Walnut, Wild Rose. Builds inner confidence and constancy.

Study and Intuition Mix. Cerato, Chestnut Bud, Clematis, Impatiens, Rock Water, Scleranthus, Vervain, White Chestnut and Wild Oat. On occasion Wild Rose may be added. Helps you focus, concentrate and study effectively with enthusiasm and without inner distractions.

Change and Bereavement Mix. Chestnut Bud, Gentian, Gorse, Heather, Honeysuckle, Mustard, Pine, Star of Bethlehem, Sweet Chestnut, Walnut, Wild Rose and Willow, also Grief (Bailey). Valuable for all who have been bereaved, even in the distant past. Also for the many changes we all face in life.

Carer's and Worry Mix. Agrimony, Centaury, Gentian, Heather, Oak, Red Chestnut and White Chestnut and Tranquillity (Bailey). For sleeplessness add Vervain. Carers often carry a heavy burden for a long time, both emotionally and physically, so Exhaustion Mix is an ideal accompaniment, to refresh and regenerate.

Exhaustion Mix. Elm, Gorse, Hornbeam, Mustard, Oak, Olive, Walnut and Wild Rose. Useful as a pick-me-up after prolonged effort; also for those with responsibilities that sometimes feel too heavy.

Gorse

Assertiveness in Leadership: Agrimony, Centaury, Cerato, Chestnut Bud, Elm, Holly, Impatiens, Red Chestnut, Rock Rose, Star of Bethlehem, Walnut and Willow.

Understanding and Balance in Leadership: Beech, Cerato, Chestnut Bud, Heather, Holly, Impatiens, Oak, Rock Water, Scleranthus, Star of Bethlehem, Vervain, Vine, Walnut and Wild Oat.

Addictions Mix. Agrimony, Cherry Plum, Crab Apple, Clematis, Gentian, Larch, Pine, Rock Rose, Star of Bethlehem, Walnut, White Chestnut and Wild Rose. Helps break psychological dependencies by strengthening emotional reserves. Insecurity is one of the deep reasons for the development of addictions. The small child overcomes the problem of insecurity by sucking its thumb. Unfortunately, it is not cool for adults to do this, so they often adopt more harmful habits! This combination will usually need Relationship Mix to follow.

Fears and Nightmares Mix. Aspen, Cherry Plum, Mimulus, Rock Rose, Star of Bethlehem, White Chestnut and Fears (Bailey). For fears, terrors and nightmares, both in adults and children.

Work Stress Mix. Gentian, Hornbeam, Impatiens, Mustard, Oak, Olive, Rock Water, Vervain, Walnut, White Chestnut. Refreshes and restores interest when stressed at work. Rescue Remedy and equivalents are also useful.

Follow-your-heart Mix. Centaury, Cerato, Chestnut Bud, Pine, Rock Water, Wild Oat. To help us to follow our intuition and the path in life that is best for us, even if it is not obvious at present. Also helps us gain wisdom from life's experiences.

Blues Mix. Gentian, Gorse, Mustard, Sweet Chestnut, Walnut, Wild Rose, Willow, Despair (Bailey). Helps lift low moods and sadness, and allows the sunshine back into life. Not instead of conventional anti-depressants if advised by a medical practitioner.

Past Abuse Mix. Agrimony, Crab Apple, Gentian, Gorse, Holly,

Mustard, Pine, Rock Rose, Star of Bethlehem, Sweet Chestnut, Walnut, Willow, Childhood and Grief (Bailey). Useful for cases of past emotional, physical and sexual abuse. Australian Bush Sexuality Essence would be useful as well for sexual abuse.

Insomnia Mix. Impatiens, Olive, Rock Rose, Vervain and White Chestnut. Useful for releasing mental and emotional patterns and excitement that prevent refreshing sleep.

Combinations supplied for Specific Circumstances

AUSTRALIAN BUSH

Abund Essence. Dissolves poverty consciousness and pessimism, bringing trust, belief in abundance and the ability to share happily.

Adol Essence. Dissolves insensitivity, sense of alienation, embarrassment, anger and a feeling that 'It's not fair', replacing these with consideration, communication, self-esteem and ability to cope with change.

Cognis Essence. Addresses confusion, daydreaming and the feeling of being overwhelmed, bringing clarity and focus.

Confid Essence. Helps shift guilt, low self-esteem, shyness, and victim mentality, bringing confidence, integrity, personal power and the qualities of taking responsibility and being true to oneself.

Dynamis Essence. Dissolves temporary loss of drive and enthusiasm and the jaded feeling, replacing this with new zest and joyful enthusiasm for life.

Femin (woman) Essence. A powerful essence for helping harmonise imbalances due to the female cycle and menopause. It replaces mood swings, weariness and self-disgust with balanced feminine stability.

Heartsong Essence. Frees the voice and opens the heart, inspiring creative and emotional expression and clarity, and confidence in public performance, singing and speaking. It dissolves blocks in your creativity and ability to express feelings.

Meditation Essence. Helps awaken connections to your deeper streams of spirituality and intuition, allowing inner guidance to come through, uncluttered by old blockages. It also stabilises and heals psychic trauma.

Relationship Essence. Enhances communication, forgiveness, the ability to express personal feelings in intimate relationships; dissolves emotional pain, confusion and resentment which often has its roots in the deep past.

Gentian

Sexuality Essence. Allows you to feel good about and accept your physical body, enhancing sensuality, passion and intimacy. It helps release shame, fear of intimacy and lack of sensitivity in sexuality.

Solaris Essence. Dissolves negative emotional effects of fire and sun.

Transition Essence. Eases fear of death and the unknown, allowing one to come to terms with the idea of death as a passing over into another dimension.

Travel Essence. Many people become drained and disorientated by travel, especially air travel. This essence helps maintain balance and refreshes you in this situation.

Crystal Herbs Combinations for Self Treatment

Addictions Release. Helps strengthen those wishing to release dependency on addictive substances.

Auric Protection. Strengthens the Auric Field and helps keep you centred in your own energy without being influenced by the thoughts and emotions of others.

Bereavement. Helps release feelings of grief and sadness at the loss of a loved one. Also helps release unexpressed grief from the past.

Concentration. Helps you focus and become centred especially if studying or taking exams.

Confidence. Enhances confidence, releasing shyness and insecurity about your abilities.

Decision Making. Centres and focuses you, enabling you to be decisive. Stops scattered thinking.

Emotional Balance. Releases tension and negative emotions, often stored in the solar plexus area. Balances and harmonises emotions after a period of stress.

Energy. Clears blockages to bring more physical energy and feelings of groundedness.

Forgiveness. Helps bring balance to the feminine nature in both male and female. Balances left and right brain, allowing more mental skills to develop and strengthening the 'doing' energy to help those needing to manifest their creativity in the world.

Inner Calm. Releases anxieties and fears, bringing calm and serenity.

Inner Joy. Releases the trapped emotions of despair and depression, replacing them with renewed joy and vitality.

Inner Peace. Helps release feelings of anger and resentment, bringing instead a smooth untroubled feeling of deep inner peace.

Letting Go. Dissolves pent-up stress, especially if received from other people. It also helps release emotional ties and the wish to manipulate or control a situation.

Masculine Balance. Helps balance the masculine energy in both male and female. Helps develop inner knowing, intuition and creativity, balancing left and right brain.

Patience. Releases impatience, tension and irritability, replacing them with tolerance and patience.

Relaxation. Helps release stress in mind and body, making it easier to rest and relax.

Sleep. Helpful in cases of insomnia, restlessness and disturbed sleep patterns.

Deva Flower Essences

Nuits Difficiles Irritabilité. Insomnia, nervousness, mental agitation. This essence calms over-excitement, restlessness, and an inability to relax and wind down. Helps bring a quiet mind, relaxation and a peaceful sleep.

Tensions Corporelles. Physical/emotional tension. Dissolves tension held within the body and emotions, bringing physical relaxation and harmony, renewed energy and vitality.

Vulnerabilité Fragilité. Vulnerability, fragility, fatigue and fears. This helps overcome fatigue, apathy, exhaustion, resignation, anxieties and feelings of rejection. It brings new vitality and confidence, enabling you to stand up to your challenges.

Vie Affective et Sexualité. Sexual troubles. Helps harmonise and balance issues related to sexuality, especially when it has become unbalanced or excessive. Facilitates healthy harmonious sexual expression as being a source of genuine communication for a couple.

Habitudes Nuisible. Dependency. Eliminates unhealthy attachments, habits and dependencies, physical and mental. Helps overcome withdrawal symptoms and regulates life rhythms and vitality.

Stress Désorientation. Modern-day stress. Many people live in environmentally stressful situations and feel distanced or dissociated as a result, or become overstimulated or exhausted. This essence helps restore equilibrium, balance and inner peace.

South African Flower Essences

Adolescent Essence. Helps ease the passage through adolescence.

Auric Protection Essence. Provides protection against negativity, negative thoughts directed against you, psychic attack and the ill-effects of radiation.

Creativity Essence. Helps you access and express your creativity in every aspect of life. Helps you to realise that you create your own reality and that your destiny is to co-create with your higher self and the spiritual realms.

Earth Essence. Helps you develop an awareness of your responsibility to Gaia, the Earth, and to Nature. You can then appreciate and understand your role in helping care for the planet as gardeners in the garden.

Inner Child Essence. Helps access the child within, to ease childhood pain and trauma, to learn to love the child who once was, who still plays such a critical role in the way the adult in us behaves and interacts.

Star of Bethlehem

Inner Female Essence. Strengthens the spiritual feminine within, bringing balance with the inner male. It allows femininity to blossom and brings harmonious interaction with women in your life.

Inner Male Essence. Strengthens the spiritual masculine within, bringing balance with the inner female and balancing yin and yang energies. It allows your masculine side to blossom and brings harmonious interaction with men in your life.

Meditation Essence. Facilitates meditation and renewed contact with your higher self, soul and spirit, allowing you to attune to your inner guidance and to that from higher realms.

Menopause Essence. Enables you to move calmly and confidently into the next chapter of life, the role of the woman of maturity and wisdom.

Parenting Essence. Allows development of nurturing skills and enables you to access guidance from your higher self in order to parent more effectively. It also enables you to parent your own inner child.

Stress Essence. For times of stress, fatigue, overwork, nervousness and depletion.

Study Essence. Facilitates the assimilation of knowledge, focusing the mind and improving your ability to concentrate. Particularly useful at exam times.

Substance Abuse Essence. Assists in breaking addictive behaviour patterns. It centres you and strengthens willpower.

Bailey Flower Essences

Childhood. Helps to free energies that have been blocked since childhood, and for those locked in childish patterns.

Despair. For those in the depths of despair, this essence brings ease and generates a renewed joy in life.

Fears. Fears can constrict much of our life. This essence helps us to let go our fears so that we can live in greater freedom.

Grief. Helpful in cases of grief and anguish where there is deep distress.

Obsession. Useful when a particular thought goes round and round and will not go away.

Possession. For those who are controlled by others, or by their beliefs, and are unable to break free.

Tranquillity. Helpful in cases where the mind is overactive, the extreme states being those of the workaholic and the depressive.

Transition. For when there are major changes in life, and when the past needs to make way for a new and better life.

Unification. This helps to unite the mind-body-spirit, helping us to break free of previous restricting beliefs and patterns.

Yang. Helps to build the outgoing 'male' power whilst bringing stronger links with the intuitive 'Yin' aspects of the personality.

Yin. The counterpart of the 'Yang' essence, this builds the intuitive wisdom aspects of the personality whilst keeping the feet firmly on the ground.

Desert Alchemy

There are over 70 combination essences in the Desert Alchemy range. The following are among the more important:

Ancestral Patterns. Facilitates release of family line and ancestral patterns.

Clearing and Releasing Formula. Activates our innate protective energies and helps release energies we have taken on from others or from the environment.

Community Spirit Formula. Enhances our ability to sensitively and firmly express our personal needs in relation to a group and to contribute inspiration to the community, including an appreciation of our place in the wider global community.

Connecting with Purpose Formula. Helps us define our purpose and then integrate it in daily life.

Creativity Formula. Helps us become inspired and connected to our creative energy without blocking ourselves with self-criticism or judgement.

Emotional Awareness Formula. Helps us feel rather than think about a situation.

Experiencing Your Feeling Formula. Allows us to feel the joy of being a human being that underlies every other emotion.

Inner Father Formula. Helps us to know inner authority and leadership qualities, and to move forward in life.

Integrating Being and Doing Formula. Helps us find the balance of stillness in action.

Owning the Level Formula. Helps bring clarity and courage to do what you most love to do.

Sexual Harmony Formula. Helps us recognise the importance of sexual energy and learn how to use it wisely and sensitively.

Transitions Formula. Allows us to be still within during times of great external changes, and to avoid becoming caught up in trivial issues.

Unconditional Love and Support Formula. Helps these qualities bloom within us and radiate from us, allowing us to recognise the supportive role the universal flow of energy gives us when we allow it to do so.

The Universe Handles the Details Formula. Allows us to flow with situations rather than try to exert control over them.

Unlocking Sexual Grace Formula. Releases deep trauma and shock stored from past experiences which have stopped us being aware of our own sexuality and body.

Findhorn Flower Essences

Life Force. Helps overcome tiredness, apathy and burnout. Restores and revitalises immunity and energy.

Clear Light. Brings about a peaceful state of mind, mental clarity and brightness. A helpful aid to meditation and contemplation.

Jetstream. Helps dissolve negative effects of travel such as sleep disturbance, body rhythm upsets and anxiety.

Revelation. Facilitates inner change and transformation, allowing fresh flows of inspiration to restore inner vitality and the ability to move forward.

Australian Living Essences

Concentration and Meditation. Helps you to focus and brings inner calm.

Creativity. Brings the talent of creativity forward.

Emotions Balance. Helps balance emotional turmoil.

Energy. Helps restore energy when feeling depleted.

Inner Strength. Brings knowledge of your ability to cope with challenges.

Relaxation. Helps you to relax after a time of tension or stress.

Top left: *Cherry Plum (Bach)*

Top right: *Agrimony (Bach)*

Bottom: *Centaury (Bach)*

Beech (Bach)

Chapter 7
Individual Essences

Fringed Violet

This chapter reviews the complete Bach system, one important range of essences from the USA and one from Australia. The Bach system is the basic introductory range for many people worldwide, but both the Masters and the Australian Bush are also 'entry level' essences.

Bach Flower Essences

Numerous makers in Britain and elsewhere

- Each essence is categorised as follows:
- Name
- Keynote describing the negative aspect which needs healing
- A brief elaboration of the negative aspect
- The positive potential released by taking the essence.

Agrimony. Brave Face, Tortured Inside. A cheerful exterior hides an inability to express inner worries and anxieties. Trying hard to keep the peace and avoid showing their inner feelings, even to themselves. Positive side is inner calm whilst honestly expressing real feelings.

Aspen. Fears of Unknown Origin. Recurrent fears, apprehension and anxieties of unknown origin. Often in children frightened of the dark or nightmares. Sometimes sudden panic attacks, perhaps with trembling or sweating. Positive side is inner strength and security.

Beech. Critical Intolerance. Rigid, critical and narrow minded, judging others in a situation. Often irritated by other people's habits. Positive side is tolerance and a greater understanding of the wider aspects of life.

Centaury. Can't Say No. Often weak willed, certainly as far as own needs are concerned, neglecting these to please and serve others. Give in easily to please others and deny themselves in order to avoid confrontation. Positive side is the ability to say No without guilt, bringing an assertiveness that allows their own needs to be met.

Cerato. Lack of Confidence to Follow Own Judgement. Although knowing what their inner wisdom is telling them, they do not trust this, and seek approval and advice from others. May follow fashion slavishly. Positive side is trusting in own inner guidance, quietly self-reliant.

Cherry Plum. Sense of Losing Control of Your Mind. Sensitive, highly-strung and easily getting to the stage of an outburst of temper and anger, wanting to scream or shout or hit someone – finding it difficult to unwind. Useful in some cases of PMT. Positive side is tremendous inner calm, being centred and connected to a deep inner resource of calm, courage and resilience.

Chestnut Bud. Repeating Mistakes in Life. Often slow learners in life, repeating the same mistakes again and again, for example staying in unhappy jobs or relationships. Failing to learn from life's experiences and forgetting them. Positive side is to be mentally flexible, picking things up quickly and learning from each of the lessons that life presents. Doing this enables rapid, successful progress on life's journey. A very useful helper essence to use regularly.

Chicory. Selfish, Possessive Love. Emotionally needy, seeking to be loving and kind only if there is a direct benefit to self. Becoming manipulative and interfering in relationships, and feeling insecure unless love, money or material things flow their way. Positive aspects are genuine generosity and unconditional love, without strings attached, and the ability to let others be themselves whilst feeling secure oneself.

Clematis. Day Dreaming. Appearing vague, dreamy and inattentive, not being fully present; mind is often elsewhere. Living in the future or a fantasy world of ideals, may appear not to hear, and feel a lack of vitality. Positive side is being mentally present and focused at all times, bringing vitality, willpower and a good memory.

Crab Apple. Feelings of Uncleanness. The 'spring clean remedy' for all levels especially if one has developed a feeling of disgust with some aspect of oneself, whether bodily (such as spots) or mind (such as obsession with trivia). The positive side is to accept oneself and others, imperfections and all, and to focus on the wider picture of life, not the smaller details.

Elm. Temporarily Overwhelmed. Strong, capable people sometimes suffer from 'the straw that breaks the camel's back', and become exhausted after a spurt of effort. Often good managers and working in positions of responsibility. Taking Elm brings back the positive qualities of unshakeable reliability and inner resilience, and restores the ability to cope.

Gentian. Depressed and Discouraged at Setbacks. Lacking faith in life and themselves and are easily discouraged and despondent when a setback occurs, or when things get difficult. Positive aspect is a positive optimistic outlook on life and a trust that everything is happening according to a perfect plan, to one's own greatest benefit.

Gorse. Hopelessness and Despair. Without any obvious setbacks, people needing Gorse have lapsed into a deep despair of 'Oh, what's the use of trying? It's all going wrong'. The positive side is renewed vigour and mental optimism in all circumstances. Particularly useful in long-term illness or relationship or job problems, where the person has lost hope of recovering.

Heather. Fussy Self-Centredness. Always worried about their own symptoms or concerns, and dominating conversations with others by talking about what interests (or worries) them. The positive aspect is the unselfish listener and helper; outward-going with a wide range of interests which will uplift others.

Orange Blossom

Holly. Jealousy, Envy, Revenge, Suspicion, Touchiness and Greed. These are negative emotions which at their strongest include hatred. The cause is a blockage that stops love flowing through a person to others. Taking Holly brings the quality of unconditional love, and an understanding perspective on life.

Honeysuckle. Living in the Past. Mentally cannot forget the past and feeling attached to it, perhaps by reason of bereavement or redundancy. Look back at happier times and do not expect such happiness again. Positive side is to release the attachments that hold one back from present or future happiness, and allow one to live positively in the here and now.

Honeysuckle

Hornbeam. Monday-Morning Feelings. Mental weariness, waking up tired and without the drive to face the day. Hornbeam types usually cope, because they are lifted by something interesting that happens, but they lack enthusiasm to motivate themselves, sometimes as a result of prolonged mental effort. Taking Hornbeam brings back a fresh lively mind and a keen interest in life and events.

Impatiens. Impatience and Irritability. Especially with others, the person needing Impatiens is quick but unforgiving; cannot see why the other person is slower in either grasp or performance. Often prefers to work alone, and poor at delegating. Temper may flare up rapidly, then die down just as quickly. The remedy brings patience, calm, tolerance and understanding of others.

Larch. Lacking Confidence. Such people feel they are not able to achieve the same things as others; expect to fail or do badly. Actually they fail only to acknowledge their own inner potential, and so do not try to draw from the inner confidence they possess. Positive side is to be in touch with your inner confidence, bringing self-esteem and ability to take the initiative.

Mimulus. Fears from Known Causes. Often timid and shy, people needing Mimulus keep their fears to themselves. These are fears, for example, of illness, accidents, poverty, spiders, and the dark. The positive side is quiet, gentle courage and an ability to face their concerns without fear.

Mustard. Deep Gloom without Cause. The Mustard type of gloom comes suddenly out of the blue, sits over one like a dark cloud, then just as quickly disappears. It can be severe and frightening. Taking Mustard brings back unshakeable joy and cheerfulness, along with inner calm.

Oak. Strong Person but Exhausted. When you have overworked and pushed yourself beyond the limit of endurance over a period of time, you become drained, exhausted and fatigued. The positive side is the return of the ability to conscientiously press on, support family, colleagues, and recognise when to delegate or take time off for refreshment.

Olive. Mental and Physical Exhaustion. Energies all spent after giving a great deal to other people or to situations over a period of time. May be at the point of tears, and everything becomes an effort. Positive side is the return of strength and vitality, and great inner energy.

Pine. Guilt and Low Self-Esteem. Pine people blame themselves for anything that goes wrong, including other people's mistakes. They may feel they deserve their lot in life, and feel unworthy of anything better. Taking Pine brings inner forgiveness and restores self-worth, allowing one to accept oneself realistically and admit one's own faults without feeling bad.

Red Chestnut. Worries about Others. People needing this essence always fear the worst: 'He might have had an accident', or other worries. Their care for others becomes clouded by personal anxiety. Health professionals as well as carers and parents often slip into this state. Taking the essence brings the ability to care with compassion and empathy but without anxiety.

Red Chestnut

Rock Rose. Terror or Strong Fear. In emergencies, there is often a feeling of panic as well as severe fear and terror. Some people who are sensitive suffer these deeper fears on unseen levels. This fear can paralyse you, or can give children nightmares. Taking Rock Rose brings tremendous inner calm and courage in all situations, even the most frightening.

Rock Water. Perfectionism. The extreme type is self-denial and self-repression, but far more commonly a state arises for people who achieve high standards. They would congratulate anyone else achieving these standards, but continue to give themselves a hard time, finding ever more work to do instead of making time to relax. Rock Water helps them to be kind and gentle to themselves, and respect their own needs.

Scleranthus. Indecisive and Uncertain. Difficulty in making decisions, or deciding between two alternatives. The mind keeps darting about, making the person unhappy, yet unwilling to ask for advice. The person is subject to changeable moods and so can be unreliable. The positive side is to bring inner balance and the ability to make a prompt decision.

Star of Bethlehem. Shock. Shock can be recent or from the more distant past, yet still leaves its stain on physical, emotional and mental levels. The body's natural healing powers can be blocked, either by a single recent or past shock, or by 'long slow shock' in a traumatic childhood. Shock brings numbness. Taking the essence dissolves the effects of shock and helps one be calm and unruffled in any emergency.

Sweet Chestnut. Desolation and Extreme Mental Anguish. Often accompanied by a feeling of aloneness, as though one is in the pit of despair, or a tunnel with no light to be seen, such that sympathy or love from another has no effect. 'The dark night of the soul'. The positive side is release from the tunnel or pit, allowing one to move positively forward with confidence, and with faith that support will always be there.

Mimulus

Vervain. Over-Enthusiasm. Vervain people think they are right, and intensely try to convert others to their point of view. They push themselves hard, expending a great deal of effort, and find it difficult to relax. Taking Vervain calms the busy mind, allowing one to relax; creates a relaxed attitude of sharing rather than inflicting one's beliefs and point of view.

Vine. Dominating and Dictatorial. Vine people know they are right and have no need to listen to anyone else. 'The chairman who manages without the committee, even when the committee is there'. Often capable, they may turn ruthless and cruel and put others down. Ideal for bullies. Taking Vine brings the positive aspects of calm, wise leadership and authority, and the ability to bring out the best in others without controlling them.

Walnut. Link-Breaker, Protecting against Outside Influences. At times, particularly when inner change is needed, it is easy to allow oneself to be shackled by old ties or restrictions, rather than letting go and moving confidently into the new situation. Particular times are house or job moves, relationship changes, bereavement, pregnancy and the menopause. Walnut protects you, allowing inner change and growth to occur, unaffected by past or present external circumstances. Helps you stay on the straight-and-narrow.

Water Violet. Superior and Aloof. These people feel superior and it drives a wedge between them and others in their own minds, causing a separation which appears as aloofness and loneliness. Although calm and capable, they may appear proud or condescending. The positive side is warm integration into society, sharing gifts of wisdom and healing with others.

White Chestnut. Persistent Unwanted Thoughts. The incessant mental chatter which goes on and on, often with one thought stuck and returning time and again, can lead to a troubled mind and lack of sleep or concentration. Taking this remedy brings calm and peace to the mind, allowing you to think clearly and positively.

Impatiens

Wild Oat. Life's True Path is Unclear. Whether at a cross-roads in life or not, there are times when we are unsure and lack direction. We may be talented but have not found the right occupation – we are uncommitted to a specific direction. Wild Oat brings a clear view of the correct direction, and helps illuminate any blockages that are stopping us from pursuing it.

Wild Rose. Apathy and Resignation. Sad and indifferent to the difficult or unpleasant circumstances they find themselves in, people needing this essence have become resigned to their fate, and have lost the willpower and spark that would help them to change it. The positive side is a lively enthusiasm for life, and renewed zest. They accomplish things easily and effortlessly, and put nothing off till tomorrow through apathy.

Willow. Bitterness and Resentment. Hard knocks in life, either to ourselves or to others, can lead firstly to dented optimism, then to a feeling of 'It's not fair' or 'Why me?' or 'Why them?' and finally to bitterness or resentment. Such emotion harboured inside is a dangerous inhibitor of the immune system and one's powers of self healing, whether it relates to recent or past hurts. The positive aspects of Willow are: restored optimism and faith in life, a forgiving nature and an understanding of personal power and responsibility.

Rescue Remedy (Nelsons), Five Flower Essence (Healing Herbs), Emergency Essence (Crystal Herbs and Sun Essences), RQ, RQ6, RQ7 (Milagra), Situations de Crise (Deva), Recovery Remedy (Ainsworths)

The classic combination, formulated by Dr Bach, consists of Cherry Plum, Clematis, Impatiens, Rock Rose and Star of Bethlehem. Some add Larimar, Self Heal or Lotus to enhance the effect. Rescue Remedy helps dissolve the emotional effects of shock, fear, accidents and emergencies; restores calm and stability.

Masters Flower Essences (California, USA)

Almond. Self-control, calmness of mind and nerves. Helps those with very active lives, who require more time in the day.

Apple. Healthfulness. To be conscious of health, vitality, joy, and energy. Also for fear of illness, and periods of discouragement, lethargy and doubt.

Apple Blossom

Avocado. Sharp memory. For when quick, clear thinking is required, or when detailed tasks are undertaken. Helps creativity.

Banana. Humility and Calm. Brings detachment and the ability to step back and observe. Dissolves emotional over-involvement in situations.

Blackberry. Purity of Thought. Counters scepticism and denial in the 'no-nonsense' type of person. Brings optimism and a positive outlook on life.

Cherry. Cheerfulness. 'The Emotional Lightener'. Dissolves moodiness, bringing an optimistic even-minded approach to life's ups-and-downs.

Coconut. Upliftment. For times of challenge or struggle, brings upliftment and a solution-orientated state of mind. Frees one from restlessness and enables one to rise mentally above the mundane.

Corn. Mental Vitality. 'The I Can Essence'. For freshness and newness, new beginnings and enthusiasm. Helps get rid of stale thoughts and old habits.

Date. Sweetness and Tenderness. Brings acceptance and tolerance of others for who they are, dissolving any tendency to judgement and criticism. Relieves loneliness, boredom and feelings that life has no meaning.

Fig. Flexibility. For people who are too hard on themselves, despite high achievements. Helps dissolve self-imposed limits by allowing appreciation of a wider perspective.

Grape. Love and Devotion. For those who feel a lack of love in their lives, to bring the innate ability to love unconditionally and selflessly. Helpful for bereavement, separation or divorce.

Lettuce. Calmness. 'The Unruffler'. Stills excited emotions, bringing inner calm before, during and after the storms of life. Helps ground and balance highly creative people.

Orange. To Banish Depression. Dissolves depression and down-heartedness, bringing an uplifting flow of energy. Can awaken the potential for great joy.

Peach. Selflessness. The 'Mother' essence. Brings concern for the welfare of others, and compassion and service to those in need. Dissolves selfishness.

Pear. Peacefulness. The 'Emergency Essence'. Helps recovery from shocks, accidents, surgery, illness and childbirth, and other times of great stress. Brings a dynamic, energetic, relaxed state of mind.

Pineapple. Self-assuredness. Dissolves insecurity, shyness and self-doubt. Brings belief in one's own abilities, and helps one feel centred and complete.

Raspberry. Kind-heartedness. For forgiveness and a sympathetic nature. Dissolves over-sensitivity and helps one get over old hurts and discords.

Spinach. Simplicity. 'The Uncomplicator'. Brings child-like trust and contentment. For stress and stress-related issues, for an overly analytical state of mind, and for people who take themselves too seriously.

Strawberry. Dignity. For self-confidence and self-esteem and strength of character. Clears guilt.

Tomato. Mental Strength and Courage. 'The Warrior Essence'. Helps one to live in the affirmation of victory over life's trials, with protection on psychic levels. Helps battling with addictions to food, smoking or any unwanted habit.

Australian Bush

The Bach and Masters sets have been both detailed in full. The following essences are some of the most important essences in the Australian Bush range.

Banksia Robur. Brings enjoyment of and interest in life, dissolving loss of drive and enthusiasm.

Billy Goat Plum. Dissolves shame, sexual revulsion and dislike or disgust with part of one's body. Brings acceptance of the physical body and relaxes one to allow sexual pleasure and enjoyment.

Black Eyed Susan. The pattern of imbalance is to be rushing, always on the go and impatient. The essence brings inner peace, and an ability to slow down, turn inward and be still.

Bush Fuchsia. Dissolves the inability to balance the logical and rational with the intuitive and creative. Stops one ignoring gut feelings. Brings a trust in, ability to follow and development of, the intuition.

Bush Gardenia. Improves communication, passion and interest in others, stopping one taking one's loved ones for granted, or being unaware of others.

Crowea. Balances and centres you, bringing you in touch with your feelings. Negative picture is feeling not quite right, out of balance or worrying.

Dagger Hakea. Brings forgiveness and open expression of feelings, removing bitterness or resentment towards close family, friends or lovers.

Five Corners. Brings love and acceptance of self, ability to celebrate one's own beauty; allows one's true self to stand out. Dissolves lack of self-esteem, low self-confidence, self-dislike and self-sabotage.

Flannel Flower. Brings gentleness, joy in all physical expression and touch, sensuality and a trust to express and reveal oneself. Removes dislike of being touched and feelings of discomfort with intimacy.

Fringed Violet. Removes the effect of past or present distress, bringing healing to the aura and our emotional aspects. Brings powerful psychic protection.

Grey Spider Flower. Dissolves terror, panic, the tendency to nightmares of unknown origin and fear of the supernatural. Brings faith, calm and courage.

Isopogon. Brings ability to learn from past experiences and to retrieve forgotten skills. Dissolves stubbornness and the controlling aspects of personality.

Jacaranda. For decisiveness, clear-mindedness and focused attention. Pattern of imbalance is being scattered, changeable, dithering, unfocused and rushing.

Kangaroo Paw. Brings a relaxed attitude, sensitivity, savoir-faire, and enjoyment of people. Helps people who are unaware of appropriate social behaviour, who are awkward, clumsy, self-centred or insensitive to other people's needs.

Little Flannel Flower. For those who are too serious or deny the 'child' within us, this essence brings playfulness, spontaneity and an ability to have fun.

Mountain Devil. For hatred, jealousy, anger, suspicion and holding of grudges. This essence brings forgiveness, happiness, inner peace and unconditional love.

Old Man Banksia. For those who are disheartened or weary, this essence brings an ability to cope with whatever life brings.

Philotheca. For those with excessive generosity or an inability to accept acknowledgement, this essence gives an ability to accept praise, acknowledgement and love, helping one feel open to abundance.

Red Grevillea. Brings boldness and the ability to withstand other people's judgements, giving the strength to leave unpleasant situations. For those who feel stuck, reliant on others or affected by their criticism.

She Oak. Dissolves emotional distress associated with infertility.

Silver Princess. For those lacking direction in life, who are aimless or despondent. Enhances motivation and a sense of life's purpose and direction.

Slender Rice Flower. Brings humility, co-operation and group harmony and a perception of beauty in others. Dissolves narrow-mindedness, prejudice and racism; helpful to those who compare themselves with others.

Southern Cross. Brings a positive attitude, enabling one to take personal power and responsibility for oneself and one's actions. Dissolves victim mentality and poverty consciousness; helpful for those who blame others.

Spinifex. Empowers through awareness and understanding of the emotional causes of disease. Removes the sense of being a victim to illness.

Sturt Desert Pea. For deep emotional hurt, pain and sadness. Triggers healthy grieving and allows letting go of deeply-held grief and sadness.

Sturt Desert Rose. Dissolves guilt and low self-esteem and stops one being easily led. Brings courage, conviction and integrity.

Sundew. For procrastination, lack of focus and the feeling of being spaced out or disconnected. Brings clarity, focus and attention to detail whilst remaining firmly grounded.

Sundew. For procrastination, lack of focus and the feeling of being spaced out or disconnected. Brings clarity, focus and attention to detail whilst remaining firmly grounded.

Tall Yellow Top. Gives a sense of belonging to those who feel isolated, alienated or lonely.

Waratah. For black despair, hopelessness or being unable to respond to a crisis. Brings courage, faith, tenacity, adaptability and the capacity to tap one's innate survival skills.

Wild Potato Bush. For those who feel weighed down and stuck; brings freedom to move on in life.

Wisteria. For women who feel uncomfortable about their sexuality or who have fears arising from past sexual abuse; or for macho males whose sexuality is out of balance. Brings trust, fulfilment and enjoyment of sexuality, openness and gentleness.

Chapter 8
The Repertory of Essences

Ivy-Leaved Toadfla

A repertory is a sort of dictionary. You analyse your symptoms or mental state, look them up in the dictionary, and find the remedies and essences that help the states described. Analysing your own symptoms is difficult at first, although most of us can spot a character defect a mile away in our friends, in our family or even in perfect strangers. We have already discussed how you might choose a remedy for yourself. The repertory in this chapter will help you. It requires that you first write down your own emotional needs, idiosyncrasies, and attitudes, and then analyse them. Perhaps one way of making this easier is to ask yourself what qualities your best friend would find in you, and what qualities they would wish to help you improve.

A piece of paper and pen, and a few quiet minutes are invaluable. You can even use the repertory to prompt you as to what to look for. When I first read the list of 38 negative states that comprise the Bach essences, I found I could easily cut out six – which left me with 32 to take! Over the next three days I narrowed down my list to sixteen. But it took a full week before I could cut the list to twelve.

Once you have determined the key aspects of yourself that you want to work on, or that are out of balance, just look up the appropriate entry in the repertory. It will tell you which remedies may help you. Once you have selected a list of remedies from the repertory, go back to Chapter 7 and check that the full remedy picture applies to you, to narrow down the choice to the most appropriate remedies. It is also worth looking in the list of combinations in Chapter 6, as these combinations save you some of the work of repertorising.

The following repertory comprises all the Bach, the Masters and the Australian Bush remedies mentioned, as these are some of the easiest systems to master in the first instance and are also widely available.

This is the format for the repertory: For each entry the first upright group of essences are suggested Bach Combinations. The first group in italics are Australian Bush, the second upright are Bach and the second in italics are the Masters.

A

Absent-mindedness see Clarity of Mind, Daydreaming

Abuse, Emotional, Effects of, see also Unloved
Past Abuse Mix, *Adol, Relationship and Sexuality Essences, Bush Gardenia, Dagger Hakea, Flannel Flower, Fringed Violet, Mountain Devil, Southern Cross, Spinifex, Sturt Desert Pea, Wisteria,* Gentian, Pine, Sweet Chestnut, Willow, *Orange, Strawberry.*

Strawberry Flower

Adaptability
Carer's and Worry Mix, Follow Your Heart Mix, *Emergency Essence, Hibbertia, Waratah,* Heather, Red Chestnut, *Coconut, Fig.*

Aggression see also Violence
Relationship Mix, Bitch Mix, Past Abuse Mix, *Adol and Relationship Essences, Dagger Hakea, Mountain Devil,* Holly, Impatiens, Vine, Willow, *Raspberry.*

Aloofness see also Reserve
Adol and Relationship Essences, Bush Gardenia, Tall Yellow Top, Water Violet, *Grape.*

Anger
Relationship Mix, Bitch Mix, Past Abuse Mix, *Adol and Relationship Essences, Dagger Hakea, Mountain Devil,* Holly, Pine, Vine, Willow, *Almond, Apple, Lettuce.*

Anguish, Mental Distress, see also Despair
Addictions Mix, Fears and Nightmares Mix, *Emergency Essence, Fringed Violet, Sturt Desert Pea, Waratah,* Sweet Chestnut, *Orange.*

Anxiety see also Apprehension, Worry
Carer's and Worry Mix, All Rescue/Emergency Essences. Red Chestnut, Vervain, *White Chestnut, Banana, Lettuce, Pear, Tomato.*

Apathy see also Resignation
Study and Intuition Mix, Exhaustion Mix, *Cognis and Dynamis Essence, Banksia Robur, Sundew,* Clematis, Gentian, Wild Rose, *Grape, Orange.*

Apprehension see also Anxiety, Worry
Fears and Nightmares Mix, *Emergency Essence,* Aspen, *Lettuce, Tomato.*

Argumentativeness
Relationship Mix, Bitch Mix, Past Abuse Mix, *Adol and Relationship Essences, Dagger Hakea, Isopogon, Mountain Devil, Southern Cross,* Beech, Holly, Pine, Vervain, Vine, *Date.*

Arrogance or Bossiness, see also Dictatorial, Superiority
Relationship Mix, Bitch Mix, *Adol Essence, Bush Gardenia, Dagger Hakea, Slender Rice Flower,* Beech, Vine, *Banana, Peach.*

Ashamed of Self, Feeling, see also Self Disgust, Unclean Feeling
Addictions Mix, *Confid and Sexuality Essences, Flannel Flower, Sturt Desert Rose,* Crab Apple, *Pineapple.*

Bereavement
Bereavement Mix, *Relationship Essence, Sturt Desert Pea,* Gorse, Walnut, Willow, *Peach.*

Bitterness see also Resentment
Relationship Mix, Bitch Mix, Past Abuse Mix, *Adol and Relationship Essences, Dagger Hakea, Mountain Devil, Southern Cross,* Holly, Vine, Willow, *Raspberry.*

Calming the Emotions see also Emotional Balance
Relationship Mix, Fears and Nightmares Mix, Past Abuse Mix, *Travel Essence,* Any Emergency or Rescue Remedy, *Crowea,* Heather, Red Chestnut, *Almond, Banana, Lettuce, Pear.*

Calming the Mind
Carer's and Worry Mix, Work Stress Mix, *Cognis Essence, Black Eyed Susan, Jacaranda, Impatiens,* Vervain, White Chestnut, *Banana, Lettuce, Spinach.*

Caring
Relationship Mix, Carer's and Worry Mix, Past Abuse Mix, *Relationship and Sexuality Essences, Bush Gardenia,* Holly, Red Chestnut, *Grape, Peach, Raspberry.*

Cheerfulness
Relationship Mix, Bereavement Mix, Work Stress Mix, Blues Mix, Past Abuse Mix, *Adol, Dynamis and Travel Essences, Banksia Robur, Old Man Banksia, Waratah,* Gentian, Mustard, Sweet Chestnut, *Cherry.*

Clarity of Mind see also Absent-Mindedness
Study and Intuition Mix, Carer's and Worry Mix, Work Stress Mix, *Cognis Essence, Black-Eyed Susan, Bush Fuchsia, Isopogon, Sundew,* Clematis, White Chestnut, *Apple, Avocado, Banana, Blackberry, Lettuce, Pineapple.*

Clinginess
Relationship Mix, *Relationship Essence,* Chicory, *Grape.*

Communication
Relationship Mix, Carer's and Worry Mix, Past Abuse Mix, Adol, *Heartsong and Relationship Essences, Bush Gardenia, Kangaroo Paw,* Heather, Impatiens, *Banana, Lettuce.*

Compassion
Relationship Mix, *Adol and Relationship Essences, Bush Gardenia, Dagger Hakea, Kangaroo Paw, Mountain Devil, Slender Rice Flower,* Heather, Vine, *Date, Peach, Raspberry.*

Complaining
Relationship Mix, Bitch Mix, *Adol and Relationship Essences,* Heather, *Blackberry, Date.*

Compulsive Behaviour
Crab Apple, Heather, *Lettuce.*

Concealed Problems
Relationship Mix, Bereavement Mix, Carer's and Worry Mix, Fears and Nightmares Mix, Past Abuse Mix, *Adol, Heartsong and Relationship Essences, Sturt Desert Pea,* Agrimony.

Concentration see also Decision making, Focus or Indecision
Study and Intuition Mix, Work Stress Mix, *Cognis Essence,*
Jacaranda, Clematis, Scleranthus, *Avocado, Lettuce.*

Confidence see also Insecurity, Shyness
Confidence Mix, *Confid Essence, Five Corners,* Gentian, Larch,
Pineapple.

Confusion
Study and Intuition Mix, Carer's and Worry Mix, Work Stress Mix,
Cognis Essence, Bush Fuchsia, Jacaranda, White Chestnut, *Avocado.*

Contentment
Relationship Mix, Bereavement Mix, Carer's and Worry Mix,
Work Stress Mix, Blues Mix, Past Abuse Mix, *Adol Essence,*
Philotheca, Tall Yellow Top, Mustard, *Cherry, Date, Peach, Pineapple.*

Control (Loss of)
Fears and Nightmares Mix, *Emergency Essence, Grey Spider Flower,*
Cherry Plum, Elm, Rock Rose, *Almond, Cherry, Corn, Date,*
Lettuce, Pear.

Coping (with Problems) see also Transition, Periods of
Relationship Mix, Carer's and Worry Mix, Exhaustion Mix,
Work Stress Mix, *Emergency Essence, Waratah,* Elm, Rock Rose,
Lettuce, Pear.

Courage
Confidence Mix, *Confid Essence, Grey Spider Flower, Sturt Desert*
Rose, Waratah, Gentian, Mimulus, Rock Rose, Sweet Chestnut,
Tomato.

Crisis see also Emergencies, Shock
Any Emergency Essence, *Fringed Violet, Grey Spider Flower,*
Waratah, Cherry Plum, Elm, Rock Rose, Star of Bethlehem,
Lettuce, Pear.

Criticism
Relationship Mix, Bitch Mix, Past Abuse Mix, *Abund, Adol and*
Relationship Essences, Slender Rice Flower, Beech, Chicory, Impatiens,
Vine, *Blackberry, Date, Fig, Grape, Peach, Raspberry.*

Cynicism
Relationship Mix, Bitch Mix, Past Abuse Mix, *Abund, Adol and Relationship Essences, Dagger Hakea, Holly, Blackberry.*

Daydreaming see also Focus
Study and Intuition Mix, *Dynamis Essence, Banksia Robur, Jacaranda,* Clematis, Chestnut Bud, Honeysuckle, White Chestnut, *Avocado.*

Decision-making, Lack of Confidence in, see also Indecision, Concentration
Confidence Mix, Study and Intuition Mix, Work Stress Mix, Follow Your Heart Mix, *Confid Essence, Bush Fuchsia, Cerato, Strawberry.*

Depression see also Despair, Despondency, Melancholy, Sadness
Important note: Seek medical advice in all cases of depression.
Relationship Mix, Bereavement Mix, Blues Mix, Past Abuse Mix, *Sturt Desert Pea, Waratah,* Gentian, Gorse, Mustard, Pine, Walnut, Sweet Chestnut, Wild Rose, *Orange, Peach.*

Dependency, Clinginess, see also Independence
Relationship Mix, *Relationship Essence, Red Grevillea,* Chicory, Walnut, *Grape.*

Desire to Please
Confidence Mix, Follow Your Heart Mix, Centaury.

Despair see also Anguish, Despondency
Blues Mix, Past Abuse Mix, *Emergency Essence, Waratah,* Agrimony, Gorse, Mustard, Sweet Chestnut, *Orange.*

Despondency, Discouragement, see also Melancholy, Sadness
Bereavement Mix, Work Stress Mix, Blues Mix, Past Abuse Mix, *Dynamis Essence, Banksia Robur, Old Man Banksia, Silver Princess, Waratah,* Gentian, Mustard, *Apple, Corn, Orange, Pineapple, Strawberry, Tomato.*

Determination
  Confidence Mix, Study and Intuition Mix, Exhaustion Mix,
  Work Stress Mix, *Dynamis Essence, Old Man Banksia, Silver
  Princess, Waratah,* Elm, Gentian, Scleranthus, *Avocado, Coconut,
  Corn, Pineapple.*

Dictatorial see also Arrogance, Dominating
  Relationship Mix, Bitch Mix, *Adol Essence,* Vine, *Date, Peach.*

Direction, Lack of, and Dissatisfaction
  Study and Intuition Mix, Follow Your Heart Mix, *Cognis, Dynamis
  and Heartsong Essences, Banksia Robur, Jacaranda,* Wild Oat.

Discouragement see Despondency

Dogmatic, Inability to See Other's Point of View
  Relationship Mix, Work Stress Mix, Vervain, *Peach.*

Dominating see also Arrogance, Dominating
  Relationship Mix, Bitch Mix, *Adol Essence,* Vine, *Peach,
  Raspberry.*

Raspberry Flower

Emergencies see also Crisis, Shock
  All Emergency and Crisis Combinations, *Fringed Violet,
  Grey Spider Flower,* Rock Rose, *Pear.*

Emotional Cleansing, Release
  Relationship Mix, Bereavement Mix, Blues Mix, Past Abuse Mix,
  Adol and Relationship Essences, Sturt Desert Pea, Crab Apple, Pine,
  Apple, Grape, Lettuce, Orange, Strawberry and many others
  depending on the exact problem.

Emotional Balance – many different essences may apply depending
  on exact nature of imbalance
  Bereavement Mix, *Confid and Adol Essences, Crowea, Five Corners,*
  Pine, Scleranthus, *Almond, Apple, Pear.*

Emotional Detachment
  Bereavement Mix, Past Abuse Mix, *Heartsong Essence, Red Grevillea,*
  Chestnut Bud, Mustard, *Avocado, Banana, Cherry, Lettuce, Spinach.*

Endurance

Exhaustion Mix, *Waratah,* Elm, Oak, Olive, *Coconut, Corn, Orange.*

Energy Boost

Exhaustion Mix, *Dynamis Essence, Old Man Banksia,* Oak, Olive, Walnut, *Corn, Orange.*

Enthusiasm

Bereavement Mix, Blues Mix, *Dynamis Essence, Banksia Robur, Old Man Banksia,* Gorse, Wild Rose, *Cherry, Corn, Orange, Spinach.*

Envy see also Greed, Jealousy

Relationship Mix, Bitch Mix, Past Abuse Mix, *Relationship Essence,* Holly, *Grape.*

Escapism, Dreaminess

Study and Intuition Mix, *Cognis Essence,* Clematis, *Coconut.*

Exhaustion, Tiredness, see also Fatigue

Exhaustion Mix, *Dynamis Essence,* Olive, *Corn.*

Expressing Feelings

Relationship Mix, Bitch Mix, Past Abuse Mix, *Adol and Relationship Essences, Dagger Hakea, Flannel Flower, Wisteria,* Gentian, Sweet Chestnut, *Date, Orange,* many others may be appropriate.

Expressing Ideas and Creativity

Confidence Mix, Study and Intuition Mix, Follow Your Heart Mix, *Cognis and Heartsong Essences, Bush Fuchsia, Wild Rose.*

Family Stress and Pressures

Relationship Mix, Bitch Mix, Past Abuse Mix, *Adol and Relationship Essences, Dagger Hakea, Mountain Devil,* Chicory, Holly, Walnut, Willow, *Almond, Banana, Blackberry, Date, Grape, Lettuce, Pear, Raspberry, Strawberry.*

Fear

Fears and Nightmares Mix, *Emergency Essence, Grey Spider Flower,* Aspen, Cherry Plum, Mimulus, Red Chestnut, Rock Rose, *Apple, Spinach, Tomato.*

Tomato Flower

Focus, Mental, see also Concentration, Decision Making, Indecision
Study and Intuition Mix, *Cognis and Travel Essences, Sundew,*
Clematis, Scleranthus, *Avocado, Blackberry, Coconut.*

Forgiveness
Relationship Mix, Past Abuse Mix, *Adol and Relationship Essences,
Dagger Hakea, Slender Rice Flower,* Beech, Holly, Vine, Willow,
Raspberry.

Frustration
Relationship Mix, Bitch Mix, Carer's and Worry Mix, *Dynamis and
Travel Essences, Banksia Robur,* Holly, Impatiens, Vervain,
Scleranthus, Wild Oat, *Almond, Blackberry, Coconut.*

G

Gloom
Blues Mix, Past Abuse Mix, *Waratah,* Mustard, *Cherry, Orange.*

Greed see also Envy, Jealousy
Relationship Mix, *Mountain Devil,* Chicory, Holly, Vine, Grape,
Peach.

Grief
Bereavement Mix, Past Abuse Mix, *Sturt Desert Pea,* Honeysuckle,
Star of Bethlehem, Walnut, Grape, *Orange, Pear.*

Guilt see also Self Esteem
Bitch Mix, Confidence Mix, *Confid Essence, Spinifex, Sturt Desert
Rose,* Honeysuckle, Pine, *Peach, Strawberry.*

H

Happiness – Many essences may be helpful; see also Contentment
Relationship Mix, Blues Mix, Past Abuse Mix, *Adol Essence, Little
Flannel Flower, Mountain Devil,* Gorse, Mustard, *Apple, Cherry.*

Hatred
Relationship Mix, Bitch Mix, Past Abuse Mix, *Adol and
Relationship Essences, Dagger Hakea, Mountain Devil,* Holly,
Raspberry.

Hesitation see also Procrastination

Confidence Mix, Study and Intuition Mix, *Dynamis and Heartsong Essences, Red Grevillea,* Gentian, *Tomato.*

Homesickness

Bereavement Mix, Honeysuckle, *Avocado.*

Hope see also Optimism

Bereavement Mix, Blues Mix, Past Abuse Mix, *Abund and Dynamis Essences, Old Man Banksia, Silver Princess, Waratah,* Gorse, Sweet Chestnut, *Apple, Cherry, Orange, Tomato.*

Humility

Relationship Mix, Bitch Mix, *Adol Essence, Slender Rice Flower,* Impatiens, *Banana.*

Humour, Lack of

Relationship Mix, Bitch Mix, Past Abuse Mix, *Little Flannel Flower,* Willow, *Blackberry, Fig, Spinach.*

Hurt, Emotional Pain

Relationship Mix, Bitch Mix, Past Abuse Mix, *Adol, Relationship and Sexuality Essences, Sturt Desert Pea,* Pine, Willow, *Pear, Raspberry.*

Hyperactivity

Work Stress Mix, *Meditation Essence, Black-Eyed Susan, Jacaranda,* Vervain, *Lettuce.*

Hypochondria see also Introversion, Self Obsession

Relationship Mix, Bereavement Mix, *Abund Essence, Southern Cross, Spinifex,* Heather, Wild Rose, Willow, *Apple, Fig.*

Heather

Illness

Bereavement Mix, Blues Mix, Past Abuse Mix, *Abund Essence, Travel Essence, Transition Essence, Old Man Banksia, Spinifex,* Crab Apple, Gentian, Gorse, Star of Bethlehem.

Impatience

Relationship Mix, Bitch Mix, Work Stress Mix, *Adol and Meditation Essences, Black-Eyed Susan,* Impatiens.

Impetuousness, Hastiness
Relationship Mix, Bitch Mix, Study and Intuition Mix, Work Stress Mix, *Adol and Meditation Essences, Black-Eyed Susan, Kangaroo Paw,* Vervain, *Lettuce, Pear.*

Inadequacy
Confidence Mix, *Confid Essence, Five Corners, Southern Cross, Sturt Desert Rose,* Centaury, Elm, Gentian, Larch, Peach, *Strawberry.*

Inattention see Focus, Concentration

Indecision see also Concentration, Focus
Confidence Mix, Study and Intuition Mix, *Cognis and Travel Essences, Jacaranda, Sundew,* Clematis, Scleranthus, Wild Oat, *Apple, Avocado, Lettuce, Strawberry.*

Independence see also Dependency
Relationship Mix, Confidence Mix, Follow Your Heart Mix, *Adol and Confid Essences, Red Grevillea, Southern Cross,* Centaury, Chicory, Larch, Walnut, *Pineapple.*

Inferiority see also Self Esteem
Confidence Mix, *Confid Essence, Hibbertia,* Larch, *Pineapple.*

Infertility, Distress associated with
Femin Essence, She Oak, Willow.

Inflexibility
Relationship Mix, Study and Intuition Mix with Vine, Work Stress Mix with Vine, *Dynamis, Femin and Travel Essences, Old Man Banksia,* Rock Water, Vine, *Fig.*

Insecurity see also Confidence
Confidence Mix, Follow Your Heart Mix, *Adol and Confid Essences, Five Corners, Southern Cross,* Centaury, Cerato, Larch, *Pineapple, Strawberry.*

Insensitivity
Relationship Mix, Bitch Mix, Past Abuse Mix, *Abund, Adol and Relationship Essences, Flannel Flower, Kangaroo Paw,* Holly, Vine, Water Violet, *Banana, Peach, Raspberry.*

Intimacy

Relationship Mix, Past Abuse Mix, *Sexuality Essence, Flannel Flower, Wisteria,* Heather, Holly, *Date, Grape, Peach, Raspberry.*

Intolerance

Bitch Mix, *Adol Essence, Slender Rice Flower,* Beech, Chicory, Impatiens, *Date, Fig, Lettuce.*

Introversion see also Hypochondria

Relationship Mix, Bereavement Mix, Carer's and Worry Mix, *Abund, Adol and Relationship Essences, Five Corners, Hibbertia,* Heather, *Almond, Peach.*

Intuition

Study and Intuition Mix, Follow Your Heart Mix, *Meditation Essence, Bush Fuchsia,* Cerato, Wild Oat, Fig, *Spinach.*

Irrational Behaviour

Fears and Nightmares Mix, Aspen, Cherry Plum.

Irritability see also Emotional Balance

Relationship Mix, Bitch Mix, Work Stress Mix, Past Abuse Mix, *Adol, Meditation and Travel Essences, Black-Eyed Susan,* Beech, Chicory, Impatiens, *Date, Raspberry.*

Isolation see also Loneliness

Relationship Mix, Confidence Mix, Past Abuse Mix, *Adol Essence, Tall Yellow Top,* Sweet Chestnut, Water Violet, *Date, Grape, Peach, Pineapple.*

Jealousy see also Envy, Greed

Relationship Mix, Bitch Mix, Past Abuse Mix, *Adol and Relationship Essences, Mountain Devil,* Holly, *Apple, Grape.*

Joy

Bereavement Mix, Blues Mix, Past Abuse Mix, *Abund Essence, Little Flannel Flower,* Gorse, *Apple, Corn, Orange, Peach, Spinach.*

L

Laughter (not guaranteed!! – many essences may help)
Relationship Mix, Bereavement Mix, Blues Mix, Past Abuse Mix, *Abund Essence, Little Flannel Flower,* Mustard, *Cherry.*

Laziness
Study and Intuition Mix, *Cognis Dynamis and Travel Essences,* Clematis, Scleranthus, Wild Oat, *Corn.*

Learning Ability
Confidence Mix, Study and Intuition Mix, Follow Your Heart Mix, *Cognis Essence, Bush Fuchsia, Isopogon,* Chestnut Bud, *Avocado.*

Lethargy
Exhaustion Mix, *Travel Essence, Old Man Banksia,* Olive, *Corn.*

Lives in the Past
Bereavement Mix, Past Abuse Mix, *Cognis Essence,* Honeysuckle.

Loneliness see also Isolation
Relationship Mix, Bereavement Mix, Past Abuse Mix, *Adol Essence, Tall Yellow Top,* Gorse, Sweet Chestnut, Water Violet, *Date, Grape, Peach.*

Love, Ability to
Relationship Mix, Bitch Mix, Past Abuse Mix, *Adol and Relationship Essences, Dagger Hakea, Mountain Devil,* Chicory, Holly, *Grape, Peach, Pear, Raspberry.*

M

Manipulative Behaviour
Relationship Mix, *Adol and Cognis Essences, Isopogon,* Chicory, *Peach.*

Melancholy see also Despair, Despondency, Sadness
Bereavement Mix, Blues Mix, *Dynamis and Travel Essences,* Mustard, *Orange.*

Memory
Study and Intuition Mix, *Cognis Essence, Isopogon,* Clematis, *Avocado.*

Mental Chatter
Study and Intuition Mix plus Agrimony, *Cognis Essence, Black-Eyed Susan,* Agrimony, White Chestnut, *Coconut.*

Mistakes, Failure to Learn From
Confidence Mix, Study and Intuition Mix, *Adol and Cognis Essences, Isopogon,* Chestnut Bud, *Avocado.*

Monday-Morning Feelings
Exhaustion Mix, Work Stress Mix plus Hornbeam, *Dynamis and Travel Essences, Old Man Banksia,* Hornbeam, *Coconut.*

Mood Swings see also Emotional Balance
Relationship Mix, Past Abuse Mix, *Adol, Femin and Travel Essences,* Mustard, Pine, Scleranthus, Willow, *Cherry.*

Mothering
Relationship Mix, *Femin and Sexuality Essences, Bush Gardenia,* Chicory, Holly, *Peach.*

Motivation
Study and Intuition Mix, *Dynamis and Travel Essences, Jacaranda, Old Man Banksia, Silver Princess, Sundew,* Scleranthus, Wild Oat, *Coconut.*

Narrow-Mindedness
Relationship Mix, Bitch Mix, *Abund, Adol and Relationship Essences, Slender Rice Flower,* Beech, Heather, *Date, Peach.*

Negativity, Clearing
Addictions Mix, *Emergency Essence, Fringed Violet,* Crab Apple, Star of Bethlehem, Walnut, *Blackberry, Grape.*

Nervous Breakdown
Addictions Mix, Fears and Nightmares Mix, *Emergency Essence, Fringed Violet, Grey Spider Flower, Waratah,* Cherry Plum, *Pear.*

Nervousness see also Confidence
Confidence Mix, *Confid and Emergency Essences, Waratah,* Impatiens, Larch, *Almond, Banana, Lettuce, Pear.*

Nightmares
Fears and Nightmares Mix, *Emergency Essence, Grey Spider Flower,* Cherry Plum, Rock Rose, White Chestnut, *Lettuce, Tomato.*

Nostalgia see also Living in the Past
Bereavement Mix, *Travel Essence,* Honeysuckle.

O

Obsession
Addictions Mix, Crab Apple, Rock Water, *Fig, Spinach.*

Optimism see also Hope
Bereavement Mix, Exhaustion Mix, Past Abuse Mix, *Femin and Travel Essences, Sturt Desert Pea,* Gorse, *Blackberry, Cherry.*

Overbearing see also Arrogance, Dominating, Dictatorial
Relationship Mix, Bitch Mix, Work Stress Mix plus Vine, *Relationship Essence,* Vervain, Vine, *Grape, Pineapple.*

Over-Excitement
Work Stress Mix, *Black-Eyed Susan,* Vervain, *Lettuce.*

Over-Reacting
Relationship Mix, Bitch Mix, *Adol and Relationship Essences,* Beech, Impatiens, Vervain, *Raspberry.*

Over-Sensitivity
Relationship Mix, Past Abuse Mix, *Adol, Femin, Meditation and Relationship Essences,* Walnut, *Lettuce, Raspberry, Strawberry.*

Overwhelmed
Exhaustion Mix, *Cognis and Emergency Essences, Waratah,* Elm, Hornbeam, *Avocado, Spinach.*

P

Panic
Fears and Nightmares Mix, *Emergency Essence, Grey Spider Flower,* Aspen, Cherry Plum, Rock Rose, *Lettuce, Pear.*

Patience see also Impatience
Relationship Mix, Bitch Mix, *Adol and Meditation Essences,* Impatiens, *Coconut, Grape, Lettuce, Pear.*

Perseverance, Tenacity, Sticking at it
Relationship Mix, Confidence Mix, Past Abuse Mix, *Femin Essence,*
Old Man Banksia, Red Grevillea, Waratah, Gentian, *Coconut,*
Orange, Tomato.

Pessimism see Optimism and also Hope

Possessiveness
Relationship Mix, *Adol Essence, Kangaroo Paw,* Chicory, *Grape,*
Peach.

Prejudice
Bitch Mix, *Adol and Relationship Essences, Slender Rice Flower,*
Beech, Water Violet, *Date, Fig, Spinach.*

Pride
Relationship Mix, Bitch Mix, *Adol and Relationship Essences,*
Slender Rice Flower, Beech, Vine, Water Violet, *Banana, Pineapple,*
Strawberry.

Procrastination see also Hesitation
Study and Intuition Mix, *Cognis and Dynamis Essences, Jacaranda,*
Sundew, Hornbeam, Larch, Scleranthus, *Coconut, Corn.*

Protection from Negative Emotions and Thoughts
Relationship Mix, Blues Mix, Past Abuse Mix, *Emergency,*
Meditation, Sexuality and Travel Essences, Fringed Violet, Red
Grevillea, Walnut, *Lettuce, Tomato.*

Rejection
Relationship Mix, Blues Mix, Past Abuse Mix, *Adol and*
Relationship Essences, Sturt Desert Pea, Gentian, Willow, *Grape,*
Pineapple, Tomato.

Relationship Problems
Relationship Mix, Bitch Mix, Bereavement Mix, Carer's and Worry
Mix, Past Abuse Mix, *Adol and Relationship Essences, Bush Gardenia,*
Dagger Hakea, Red Grevillea, Sturt Desert Pea, Sturt Desert Rose,
Chestnut Bud, Chicory, Holly, Pine, Willow, *Almond, Banana,*
Date, Grape, Lettuce, Pear, Raspberry, Strawberry.

Relaxation
Carer's and Worry Mix plus Impatiens and Vervain, *Meditation and Emergency Essences, Black-Eyed Susan, Crowea, Jacaranda,* Impatiens, Vervain, White Chestnut, *Coconut, Fig, Pear.*

Resentment see also Bitterness
Relationship Mix, Bitch Mix, *Adol and Relationship Essences, Dagger Hakea, Mountain Devil,* Holly, Vine, Willow, *Raspberry.*

Reserve see also Aloofness
Follow Your Heart Mix plus Water Violet, *Adol Essence, Tall Yellow Top,* Water Violet.

Resignation see also Apathy
Exhaustion Mix, Blues Mix, *Dynamis and Femin Essences, Old Man Banksia, Silver Princess,* Gorse, Wild Rose, *Corn, Orange.*

Responsibility
Carer's and Worry Mix, Exhaustion Mix plus Scleranthus, Work Stress Mix, *Meditation Essence,* Scleranthus, *Apple, Date, Peach, Pineapple, Raspberry, Strawberry.*

Restlessness
Study and Intuition Mix, Carer's and Worry Mix, Fears and Nightmares Mix, *Dynamis and Emergency Essences, Black-Eyed Susan, Jacaranda,* Agrimony, Scleranthus, *Almond, Coconut, Lettuce, Peach.*

Rigidity see also Inflexibility
Bitch Mix plus Rock Water, Study and Intuition Mix, *Hibbertia,* Beech, Rock Water, Water Violet, *Date, Fig, Spinach.*

S

Sadness see also Depression, Melancholy
Blues Mix, Past Abuse Mix, *Dynamis and Travel Essences, Sturt Desert Pea,* Gentian, Mustard, *Apple, Cherry, Orange.*

Scattered Thoughts see Focus.

Self Criticism
Confidence Mix, *Adol Essence, Five Corners,* Chestnut Bud, Pine, *Blackberry, Pineapple, Spinach, Strawberry.*

Self Denial

Study and Intuition Mix, Work Stress Mix, Follow Your Heart Mix, *Abund Essence, Hibbertia,* Rock Water, *Fig.*

Self Discipline

Follow Your Heart Mix plus Vervain, *Hibbertia,* Rock Water, Vervain, *Almond, Fig, Pineapple, Spinach.*

Self Disgust see also Ashamed of Self

Addictions Mix, *Adol and Sexuality Essences, Flannel Flower,* Crab Apple, *Date, Strawberry.*

Self Esteem see also Guilt, Inferiority

Confidence Mix, Past Abuse Mix, *Adol and Confid Essences, Five Corners, Sturt Desert Rose,* Gentian, Pine, *Apple, Blackberry, Fig, Pineapple, Strawberry.*

Selfishness

Relationship Mix, Bitch Mix, *Adol, Relationship and Sexuality Essences, Bush Gardenia, Kangaroo Paw,* Beech, Chicory, Heather, *Peach, Raspberry.*

Self Obsession see also Hypochondria

Relationship Mix, Bereavement Mix, *Adol and Confid Essences,* Heather, *Apple, Fig.*

Self Pity

Relationship Mix, Past Abuse Mix, *Adol and Confid Essences, Southern Cross, Spinifex,* Chicory, Pine, Willow, *Cherry, Orange, Pineapple.*

Self Reproach

Relationship Mix, Bitch Mix, Confidence Mix, Follow Your Heart Mix, Past Abuse Mix, *Adol and Confid Essences, Five Corners, Sturt Desert Rose,* Pine, *Fig, Pineapple.*

Self Worth

Relationship Mix, Confidence Mix, Past Abuse Mix, *Adol and Confid Essences, Five Corners, Sturt Desert Rose,* Gentian, Pine, *Apple, Pineapple, Strawberry.*

Sexual Abuse
Past Abuse Mix, *Sexuality Essence, Flannel Flower, Fringed Violet, Wisteria,* Holly, Pine, Sweet Chestnut, Star of Bethlehem, Willow, *Banana, Grape, Date, Pear, Strawberry.*

Shock see also Crisis, Emergency
All Emergency, Crisis and Rescue Remedies, Star of Bethlehem, *Pear.*

Shyness see also Confidence
Confidence Mix, *Adol and Confid Essences,* Centaury, Larch, Mimulus, *Banana, Pineapple, Strawberry, Tomato.*

Simplicity
Study and Intuition Mix, *Jacaranda, Spinach.*

Sleep
Sleep Mix comprising Agrimony, Impatiens, Rock Rose, Vervain, White Chestnut, *Almond, Coconut, Lettuce.*

Spaced-out Feeling see also Focus
Study and Intuition Mix, *Travel Essence, Crowea, Sundew,* Clematis, *Avocado, Strawberry.*

Strength
Exhaustion Mix, *Travel Essence,* Elm, Oak, Olive, *Apple, Banana, Coconut, Corn, Pear, Tomato.*

Stress
Relationship Mix, Carer's and Worry Mix, Exhaustion Mix, Work Stress Mix, *Dynamis, Emergency and Travel Essences, Black-Eyed Susan, Crowea,* Agrimony, Elm, Gentian, Impatiens, Mustard, Olive, Pine, Rock Water, Vervain, Walnut, *Almond, Corn, Lettuce, Pear, Spinach, Tomato.*

Suicidal Thoughts – strongly advised to seek medical attention
Fears and Nightmares Mix, Blues Mix plus Cherry Plum, *Emergency Essence, Waratah,* Cherry Plum, Sweet Chestnut.

Superiority see also Arrogance, Dominating
Relationship Mix plus Water Violet, Bitch Mix plus Water Violet, *Hibbertia,* Vine, Water Violet, *Banana.*

Top: *Red Chestnut (Bach)*

Bottom: *Larch (Bach)*

Blue Hyacinth (Ilminster Essences)

Temper
Relationship Mix, Bitch Mix, Past Abuse Mix, *Adol and Relationship Essences, Dagger Hakea, Mountain Devil,* Cherry Plum, Holly, Impatiens, Vervain, Vine, *Date, Raspberry.*

Tenderness
Relationship Mix, Bitch Mix, Past Abuse Mix, *Relationship and Sexuality Essences, Flannel Flower, Kangaroo Paw,* Holly, *Date.*

Terror
Fears and Nightmares Mix, *Emergency Essence, Grey Spider Flower,* Cherry Plum, Rock Rose, *Tomato.*

Tiredness see also Exhaustion
Exhaustion Mix, *Dynamis Essence, Banksia Robur,* Hornbeam, Oak, Olive, Wild Rose, *Apple, Corn, Orange.*

Tolerance see Intolerance

Transition, Periods of – helps ease through change times and coping with problems
Relationship Mix, Confidence Mix, Bereavement Mix, Addictions Mix, Work Stress Mix, Blues Mix, Past Abuse Mix, *Dynamis and Travel Essences, Old Man Banksia,* Walnut.

Trapped, Feeling
Bereavement Mix, *Heartsong Essence, Red Grevillea, Spinifex,* Honeysuckle, Larch, Sweet Chestnut, *Orange, Pineapple, Strawberry.*

Trauma
Addictions Mix, Fears and Nightmares Mix, *Emergency Essence, Fringed Violet,* Star of Bethlehem, *Pear.*

Trust
Confidence Mix, Carer's and Worry Mix, Follow Your Heart Mix, *Adol Essence, Flannel Flower, Southern Cross,* Centaury, Cerato, Larch, Red Chestnut, *Lettuce, Spinach.*

Uncertainty as to Direction
Follow Your Heart Mix, *Cognis Essence, Jacaranda,* Wild Oat.

Unclean, Feeling, see also Ashamed of Self, Self Disgust
Addictions Mix, Past Abuse Mix, *Sexuality Essence, Flannel Flower,*
Wisteria, Crab Apple, *Apple, Blackberry.*

Understanding Problems
Relationship Mix, Confidence Mix, Bereavement Mix, Past Abuse
Mix, *Adol and Cognis Essence,* Chestnut Bud, Pine, *Peach, Raspberry,*
and others as appropriate.

Unloved, Inability to Accept Love
Relationship Mix, Bitch Mix, Past Abuse Mix, *Abund and Sexuality*
Essences, Philotheca, Sturt Desert Pea, Holly, Pine, *Grape, Strawberry.*

V

Victim Mentality
Relationship Mix, Bitch Mix, Bereavement Mix, Past Abuse Mix,
Adol Essence, Southern Cross, Spinifex, Pine, Willow, *Raspberry,*
Tomato.

Violence see also Aggression
Relationship Mix plus Cherry Plum, Bitch Mix plus Cherry Plum,
Past Abuse Mix plus Cherry Plum and Vine, *Adol and Relationship*
Essences, Dagger Hakea, Mountain Devil, Cherry Plum, Holly, Vine,
Willow, *Pear.*

Vitality see also Fatigue
Exhaustion Mix, *Dynamis and Travel Essences,* Olive, *Corn.*

W

Willpower
Confidence Mix, Study and Intuition Mix, Follow Your Heart Mix,
Travel Essence, Banksia Robur, Hibbertia, Jacaranda, Sundew,
Centaury, Cerato, Rock Water, Scleranthus, *Coconut, Corn,*
Pineapple, Tomato.

Worry see also Anxiety, Apprehension
Carer's and Worry Mix, *Emergency Essence, Crowea,* Agrimony,
Red Chestnut, Vervain, White Chestnut, *Lettuce, Peach.*

Chapter 9
Hints to Get Started

Be Proactive

Bluebell

Ask a hundred adults how they feel. They will nearly all say 'Fine'.
Yet below the surface there is often a veritable torrent of chaotic
emotions. This is true for all of us, because part of the mind's way of
coping is to bury or put off the resolution of powerful emotions that
are 'too hot to handle'. So if we want to actually heal ourselves, it is
well worth while to be proactive, that is, to search for areas of
ourselves that deserve healing – and to keep searching and searching
until no more hurt is left.

I can now admit that I am an addict to this process. I've been taking
flower essences daily for at least five years, always chosen by dowsing.
I keep finding more bits to heal. Of course I still may have my crabby
days, but the journey of healing and releasing baggage I didn't even
realise I was carrying, let alone the stuff I knew was there, has added
a tremendous extra dimension to the journey of life.

Healing Flower Essences for You

The exciting new field of flower essence therapy offers the potential
for personal transformation. Emotional well-being can be achieved
without excessive pain. Full healing of much of the baggage and
conditioning that we all carry is allowed to take place. This releases
tension held in both the emotional and the physical body, allowing us
to feel lighter and happier, calmer and brighter.

Each flower essence catalyses the healing of a particular emotional
imbalance, and is best used for the particular state diagnosed. When
starting with flower essence therapy it often seems that many essences
are appropriate. It is always worth choosing the two or three that
seem most appropriate to your current emotional needs.

We all have layers of emotion buried deep within us, and treating one layer effectively may on occasion immediately unmask a deeper layer.

> Felicity took Gentian, Hornbeam, Pine, Sweet Chestnut and Wild Oat for her current difficulties for two weeks, and felt much better from the immediate problems. However, she found herself in a stable but melancholy state which entirely reflected how she had felt from age 13 to 17, years when her mother had been ill and slowly dying. Gorse, Mustard, Walnut and Wild Rose and others dissolved this layer, to restore her to a happy normal state.

Many of us have a layer of bitterness and enmity presumably from somewhere in childhood or an unhappy relationship. These layers do not always occur in a particular order. They must each be recognised and dealt with as they present. Holly, Pine, Vine and Willow will help.

Getting Started

The following suggestions are set out as guidelines only. There are several combinations that all of us may benefit from, since everyone has similar experiences at an emotional level throughout life. We have all experienced the withholding of love at some point in our lives, the feeling that we are not quite good enough or that it is our fault. We have all experienced the hard knocks that make us feel life isn't fair. As a starting combination, **Holly, Pine, Vine** and **Willow** make a powerful set to address these issues which are common to all of us. It is worth taking four times daily for four weeks minimum, possibly with **Australian Bush Adol Essence.**

At times in childhood we felt unloved, separate and unhappy. A course of **Chicory, Gentian, Gorse** and **Sweet Chestnut** can help address this aspect of the emotional broken glass we all have within us.

Beyond these issues, many of us live in some degree of fear and insecurity, whether personal or more general – fear about world disasters, fear of illness, for example. The Bach combination to work on this level is **Aspen, Cherry Plum, Mimulus, Rock Rose** and **Star of Bethlehem,** again for 3-4 weeks. At the same time, taking **Australian Bush Emergency Essence** is appropriate. Not everybody will choose initially to take this combination, although the **Star of Bethlehem** is one that, if missed out now, should be included in the fourth set.

All of us have also experienced loss – loss of a loved one, loss of security, and change which brought sadness. To help us heal these areas of our lives, the next combination to take, following straight on from the previous, is **Gorse, Mustard, Star of Bethlehem, Walnut, Wild Rose** and **Willow.** Add in **Gentian, Pine** and **Sweet Chestnut** if not already taken. To these could be added **Australian Bush Relationship Essence.** Again, take this four times a day for at least four weeks.

During and after taking these combinations you may notice profound changes in yourself. All sorts of forgotten or painfully remembered past events may come to mind, only in a different light – a more comfortable light. You may experience the shedding of long-repressed tears. A variety of emotions may be released from deep within you and come to the surface to be acknowledged and released as the emotional memory banks are cleansed and healed. If you feel there is any deep anger or impatience in your character, carry on with **Beech, Holly, Impatiens, Vine** and **Willow.**

Many of us worry about ourselves and others. Try **Chicory, Heather, Red Chestnut** and **White Chestnut** for a while. People with long-term responsibilities either at home or work benefit from **Heather** and **Red Chestnut,** the **Carer's Combination.** You might keep a diary or notebook during this time to help you remember and then reflect upon any event that comes to mind.

Another combination that can be useful is the one to help restore your curiosity, individuality and ability to be guided intuitively. This comprises **Cerato, Chestnut Bud, Heather, Red Chestnut,**

Scleranthus and **Wild Oat.** Small children always ask 'Why?' Adults don't! This combination will help restore your curiosity! The related Australian Combinations are **Cognis and Meditation Essences.**

Businessmen often find **Vervain, Walnut, Rock Water** and **Oak** helpful, taken perhaps for one week every month. This set is also useful for enthusiasts and visionaries!

Any woman who has ever had a miscarriage or termination of pregnancy is likely to be helped by **Gorse, Red Chestnut** and **Willow,** as feelings about motherhood are otherwise clouded by unhealed emotions surrounding the original event.

The **Australian Bush Combinations** are particularly helpful for 'painting by numbers', as the above technique is sometimes known. A four weeks' course of either **Relationship Essence** or **Adol Essence,** followed by four weeks of **Sexuality Essence** is a powerful means of addressing many of the subconscious issues that we all carry, containing as they do a total of ten important essences. Other combinations can then be used as you feel appropriate.

*   *   *   *   *

Choosing essences really is the difficult part, though it is worth persevering. Here are some hints to help you get started. Many local suppliers will now make up a bottle of combinations, inexpensively.

Relationship Mix. Beech, Chicory, Gentian, Heather, Holly, Impatiens, Mustard, Pine, Red Chestnut, Sweet Chestnut, Vine, Walnut, Willow. For clear honest communication and forgiveness.

Bitch Mix. Beech, Cherry Plum, Holly, Impatiens, Pine, Vine and Willow. For irritability both premenstrually and for any wish to dominate, for control or for jealousy, negativity and bitterness or resentment.

Confidence Mix. Agrimony, Centaury, Chestnut Bud, Gentian, Larch, Pine, Sweet Chestnut, Walnut, Wild Rose. Builds inner confidence and constancy.

Study and Intuition Mix. Cerato, Chestnut Bud, Clematis, Impatiens, Rock Water, Scleranthus, Vervain, White Chestnut and

Wild Oat. On occasion Wild Rose may be added. Helps you focus, concentrate and study effectively with enthusiasm and without inner distractions.

Bereavement Mix. Chestnut Bud, Gentian, Gorse, Heather, Honeysuckle, Mustard, Pine, Star of Bethlehem, Sweet Chestnut, Walnut, Wild Rose and Willow, also Grief (Bailey). Valuable for all who have been bereaved, even in the distant past. Also for the many changes that we all face in life.

Carer's and Worry Mix. Agrimony, Centaury, Gentian, Heather, Oak, Red Chestnut and White Chestnut and Tranquillity (Bailey). For sleeplessness add Vervain. Carers often carry a heavy burden for a long time, both emotionally and physically, so Exhaustion Mix is an ideal accompaniment, to refresh and regenerate.

Exhaustion Mix. Elm, Gorse, Hornbeam, Mustard, Oak, Olive, Walnut, Wild Rose and Dynamis Essence. Useful as a pick-me-up after prolonged effort; also for those with responsibilities that sometimes feel too heavy.

Assertiveness in Leadership: Agrimony, Centaury, Cerato, Chestnut Bud, Elm, Holly, Impatiens, Red Chestnut, Rock Rose, Star of Bethlehem, Walnut and Willow.

Understanding and Balance in Leadership: Beech, Cerato, Chestnut Bud, Elm, Heather, Holly, Impatiens, Oak, Rock Water, Scleranthus, Star of Bethlehem, Vervain, Vine, Walnut and Wild Oat.

Addictions Mix. Agrimony, Cherry Plum, Crab Apple, Clematis, Gentian, Larch, Pine, Rock Rose, Star of Bethlehem, Walnut, White Chestnut, Wild Oak. Helps break psychological dependencies by strengthening emotional reserves. Insecurity is one of the deep reasons for the development of addicitons. This combination will usually need Relationship Mix to follow.

Fears and Nightmares Mix. Aspen, Cherry Plum, Mimulus, Rock Rose, Star of Bethlehem, White Chestnut and Fears (Bailey). For fears, terrors and nightmares, both in adults and children.

Work Stress Mix. Gentian, Hornbeam, Impatiens, Mustard, Olive,

Rock Water, Vervain, Walnut, White Chestnut. Refreshes and restores interest when stressed at work. Rescue Remedy and equivalents are also useful.

Follow Your Heart Mix. Centaury, Cerato, Chestnut Bud, Pine, Rock Water, Wild Oat. To help us follow our intuition and the path in life that is best for us, even if it is not obvious at present. Also helps us gain wisdom from life's experiences.

Blues Mix. Gentian, Gorse, Mustard, Sweet Chestnut, Walnut, Wild Rose, Willow, Despair (Bailey). Helps lift low moods and sadness; allows the sunshine back into life. Not instead of conventional anti-depressants if advised by a medical practitioner.

Past Abuse Mix. Agrimony, Crab Apple, Gentian, Gorse, Holly, Mustard, Pine, Rock Rose, Star of Bethlehem, Sweet Chestnut, Walnut, Willow, Childhood and Grief (Bailey). Useful for cases of past emotional, physical and sexual abuse. Australian Bush Sexuality Essence would be useful as well for sexual abuse.

Insomnia Mix. Impatiens, Olive, Rock Rose, Vervain and White Chestnut. Useful for releasing mental and emotional patterns and excitement that prevents refreshing sleep.

* * * * *

Being Your Real Self – Healthy Emotions

What stops us being our real selves? We do. If we try, we can all touch and hold on to the calm, peaceful, contented island that is our birthright. What usually happens is that we mistake this sea of emotions for reality. If by some good fortune we have no problem emotions of our own, there's always someone ready to dump his or her on to us. If we've managed to avoid these too, well there's always the nine o'clock news or the ten o'clock news or the radio or the papers! But we don't have to make the 'sea' our reality.

So how do we get to that tranquil island that lies within each of us? And how do we make that island free of any shackles from the past, free from any misconceptions about ourselves and our relationships –

in fact, free from any blockage to health and wholeness? For health and wholeness *is* that Island of Harmony and the Sea of Emotion is one of the biggest obstacles to remembering the Island. Flower essences can help us reach the Island of Harmony.

An Alternative Starting Approach

There are several stages on the road to health and wholeness, some of which can be undertaken simultaneously.

The first is to remove current emotional baggage. Often this needs Mustard, Olive, Rock Water, Vervain, Walnut, Gorse, Heather, taken perhaps for up to four weeks in order to achieve maximum effect.

Next, clear the past. The most recent episode of unhealed memory needs healing first, through the appropriate Bach Remedies. There will be different essences for different layers of unhealed memories, for example: Mustard, Walnut for memories from 3-4 years ago; Mustard, Walnut, Willow for memories from 25 years ago; Holly, Vine, Willow, for memories from 6-8 years ago. You could try dowsing for the appropriate essences for different time-frames.

It is important to heal all past memories held within the mind/body. This releases the dead weight that handicaps the body's powers of self-healing. A state of bitterness or resentment which is held long-term is particularly destructive. The resentment held within can slowly 'eat away' at your ability to be healthy.

Remember the healthy resolution of any challenge. Use this sequence:

- Accept

- Acknowledge

- Forgive

- Release

- Move on.

Next, find your path in life. Cerato helps you listen to your inner voice. Wild Oat helps your pathway in life become clearer to you. A check for full healing could be to look at yourself and ask,

'Do I accept myself fully, past, present, and for my full potential?'
If there is any hesitation then ask yourself why you hesitate. Identify
the source of the doubt, examine it, ask yourself if you wish your
growth to continue being limited by it and then, if appropriate, use
the Accept, Acknowledge, Forgive, Release, Move on sequence. Never
forget that you have done extremely well to get this far on the path
of life, and never, never doubt yourself. You can draw to yourself and
from within yourself everything you need, in order to go beyond your
challenges. Self-doubt is merely an illusion that can be melted by the
power of self-knowledge. One of the inscriptions from the Ancient
Greeks' on the famous temple at Delphi said 'Know thyself'.

Common Remedy Uses

To dissolve outward hostility: Holly, Impatiens, Vine, Willow.

To dispel an inward negative state, sadness, unhappiness:
Gorse, Mustard, Sweet Chestnut, Walnut, Wild Rose.

For faith: Gentian to give faith in self and life; Larch for lots of
confidence.

To conquer fear: Aspen, Mimulus.

To conquer terror: Cherry Plum, Rock Rose.

For full joy: Gorse, Mustard, Walnut, Wild Rose.

For full confidence: Gentian, Larch.

To help release the past: Honeysuckle, Walnut.

To dispel worry: Heather (about yourself), Red Chestnut
(about others), White Chestnut.

To dissolve deep hostility: Holly, Vine, Willow, Impatiens.

To find your path and listen to your inner voice: Cerato, Wild Oat.

For acute distress: Rescue Remedy.

For children feeling separate or alone: Gentian, Pine, Sweet Chestnut.

To gain full wisdom from daily life: Chestnut Bud.

To calm the busy mind: Vervain.

To stop giving yourself a hard time: Rock Water.

To dissolve fatigue and weariness: Olive.

For a person who puts on a brave face but is tortured inside: Agrimony.

To help you say No: Centaury.

To bring you back down to earth when dreamy or unfocused: Clematis.

To help you accept your own and others' imperfections: Crab Apple.

For people who know they are right, so don't bother arguing: Vine.

For 'It's not fair', 'Why me/them?' or bitterness or resentment: Willow.

What we all carry

Rachel is 43 years of age. She came with unresolved distress about a termination of pregnancy which happened some years previously. When she discussed her feelings about this, it became clear that the Bach Remedies to help her were Gorse, Red Chestnut and Willow. But that was only for the present moment. At a deeper level lay feelings of low self-esteem, despair and uncertainty as to life's direction: Pine, Sweet Chestnut, and Wild Oat. As a person, she drove herself hard: Rock Water. And an inability to listen to her intuition: Cerato.

Deeper still lay the unresolved issues from her past. Fourteen years previously she had two family deaths: Gorse, Mustard, Walnut. Two years before that she had moved to her present house, away from friends: Mustard, Walnut, Willow.

Twenty-seven years ago, a stillbirth. Rock Rose, Star of Bethlehem and Willow are all appropriate for such an event, even many years later, for the emotion is still held frozen within us. Gorse and Red Chestnut are often useful too. Often ill long term: Gorse, Walnut and Willow.

So, in fact, for Rachel, there were several layers of emotional healing which could be undertaken simultaneously. And the same holds true for many of us. Most people benefit from a long course of Gorse, Mustard, Sweet Chestnut, Walnut, Wild Rose and Willow. Although the events that affect us differ from person to person, the residual emotional scar (which most of us do not notice) is similar. Hence the same combinations of remedies will release much of the broken glass we each may carry.

We all carry unhealed emotional pain. By using flower essences we can choose to allow raw and unhealed emotions to resolve, in a powerful yet gentle way, even years after the event. Can we afford not to?

To make up a dropper bottle, fill a 10ml dropper bottle with 9ml fresh (not boiled) water and 1ml brandy or vodka – just to preserve it. Next, put 3 drops of each of your chosen essences into your treatment bottle, taking care to hold the dropper above the level of your treatment bottle rim. Replace the droppers on the stock bottle, finger tight. When you have put all the remedies in, replace the top, hold the bottle and bless it, perhaps asking that it should work for your highest good. Your treatment bottle is now ready to use.

Without licking the dropper, drop 2 or 3 drops of your remedies on to your tongue. Repeat 4-6 times daily for up to 4-6 weeks.

Compatibility and Side Effects

Flower essences are compatible with all allopathic and complementary medicines. On occasion, allopathic, homeopathic, herbal or other approaches may be more appropriate than essence therapy. Side effects to flower essences are rare and generally limited to intolerance to the brandy carrier. These may be headaches, nausea or heartburn, each of which I have seen, though rarely.

A few individuals, when starting essence therapy, have headaches. The mechanism of this is possibly that many of us carry a large load of toxic emotions, chemicals, and nutritional imbalances. When a healing process is first initiated by a catalyst such as a flower essence, the body heaves a sigh of relief and exhibits symptoms of release, just as some people work flat out all week, then wonder why they get a migraine at the weekend. Of course, it is only when your foot is taken off the accelerator pedal that you can hear the rattles you have been able to ignore. Nausea and heartburn appear to occur only in people who may be intolerant to brandy in particular, or to alcohol in general. To minimise these effects, either slow your rate of taking the essences, or put them on the front of your wrists direct from the stock bottle.

Another seeming side effect is a change in emotional state for the worse, perhaps toward crying or agitation, or the experiencing of a buried or unresolved emotion such as grief. If you experience this, it is worth taking time to look quietly at the emotions that are surfacing, for usually they hold a clue as to their origin. They are coming from within, often from long-forgotten depths. Take time and reflect quietly on the meaning of these emotions to you, and the wisdom they may bring you as they resolve. A friend to discuss issues or support you may be helpful; also, changing the dosage rate to just once a day, perhaps at a quiet time such as evening, can be of benefit.

As submerged feelings surface, occasionally causing turmoil, one of the Rescue or Emergency Essences may be needed for a short while. Walnut and Chestnut Bud are also useful stabilisers to take. This is not so much a side effect as a healing crisis of buried emotions that are surfacing. Most people never experience this phenomenon, but it is important to be aware of it.

Chapter 10
Resources

Books

Lazy Man's Guide to Life

Bach, Dr Edward, *Heal Thyself,* Saffron Walden: CW Daniel 1931.
Bailey, Dr Arthur, *Anyone Can Dowse for Better Health* (recommended), Cippenham: Quantum 1999.
Berne, Dr Eric, *Games People Play,* Penguin 1964.
Caddy, Eileen, *Opening Doors Within,* Forres: Findhorn Press 1987.
Carlsbad, Stuart Wilde, *Affirmations,* CA: Hay House 1987.
Carson, Louise Hay, *You Can Heal Your Life,* CA: Hay House 1984.
Chopra, Dr Deepak, *The Seven Spiritual Laws of Success,* San Rafael: Amber-Allen & New World Library 1994.
Cooper, Diana, *Light Up Your Life,* Bath: Ashgrove 1991.
Covey, Dr Stephen, *The Seven Habits of Highly Effective People,* London: Simon & Schuster 1984.
Graves, Tom, *Elements of Pendulum Dowsing,* Shaftesbury: Element 1990.
Gray, Dr John, *Men Are From Mars, Women From Venus,* London: Thorsons, 1993.
Holbeche, Soozi, *Changes,* London: Piatkus 1997.
Johnson, Rex and Swindley, David, *Awaken Your Inner Power,* Shaftesbury: Element 1995.
Lindenfield, Gael, *Self Esteem,* London: Thorsons 1995.
Redfield, James, *The Celestine Vision,* New York: Bantam 1997.
Siegel, Bernie, *Prescriptions for Living,* New York: HarperCollins 1998.

Bach Remedies

Bach, Dr Edward, *The Twelve Healers,* Saffron Walden: CW Daniel 1933.
Ball, Stephan, *Flower Remedies,* Leicester: Bookmart 1996.
Barnard, J. & M., *The Healing Herbs of Edward Bach,* Bath: Ashgrove 1994.
Barnard, Julian, *Guide to the Bach Flower Remedies,* Saffron Walden: CW Daniel 1979.
Howard, Judy, *Bach Remedies Step by Step,* Saffron Walden: CW Daniel 1995.
Howard, Judy and Ramsell, John, *The Original Writings of Edward Bach,* Saffron Walden: CW Daniel 1990.

Salmon, Philip and Jeoffroy, Anna, *Dr Bach's Flower Remedies and the Chakras,* New Barnet: Energy Works 1998.
Scheffer, Mechthild, *Bach Flower Therapy,* London: Thorsons 1990.
Wheeler, F.J., *Bach Remedies Repertory,* Saffron Walden: CW Daniel 1952.
Wildwood, Christine, *Flower Remedies,* Shaftesbury: Element 1992.

Flower Essence Therapy

Barnard, Julian, *Patterns of Life Force,* Hereford: Bach Educational Programme 1987.
Boog, Gustavo and Boog, Magdalena, *Energiza Sua Empresa* (Flower Essences in Business – in Portuguese) Sao Paulo: Edition Gente 1997.
Gurudas, *Flower Essences and Vibrational Healing,* San Rafael: Cassandra Press 1983.
Harvey, Clare G. and Cochrane, Amanda, *Encyclopaedia of Flower Remedies,* London: Thorsons, 1995
Kaminski, Patricia, *Choosing Flower Essences, an Assessment Guide,* Nevada City: Flower Essence Society 1994.
Kaminski, Patricia, *Flowers That Heal – How to use Flower Essences,* Dublin: Newleaf 1998.
Ogawa, Masanobu, *Flower Essences of the World* (in Japanese), Tokyo 1999.
Titchiner, Monk, Potter and Staines, *New Vibrational Essences of Britain and Ireland,* Halesworth: Waterlily Books 1997.
Wright, Machaelle Small, *Flower Essences,* Warrenton: Perelandra 1988.

Flower Essence Systems

Bailey, Dr Arthur, *Flower Essences Handbook,* Ilkley: Bailey Flower Essences 1997.
Barnao, Vasudeva and Kadambii (Australian Living FEs), *Australian Flower Essences for the 21st Century,* Scarborough: Australasian Flower Essence Academy 1997.
Devi, Lila (Masters), *Essential Flower Essence Handbook,* Nevada City: Master's Flower Essences 1996.
Garbely, Mary (New Zealand FEs), *A New Perception,* Titirangi, 1995.
Griffin, Judy PhD (Petite Fleur), *Remember Me To The Roses,* Fort Worth: Herbal Essence Pub 1997.
Johnson, Steve (Alaskan FEs), *The Essence of Healing,* Homer: Alaskan Flower Essence Project 1996.
Kaminski, Patricia and Katz, Richard (F.E.S.), *Flower Essence Repertory,* Nevada City: Flower Essence Society 1986.
Korte, Andreas and Hofman, A. & H., *Amazonian Gem & Orchid Essences,* Forres: Findhorn Press 1997.
Kumara, Shimara (Crystal Herbs), *The Flowers of Life,* Hoxne: Golden Ray Pubs 1997.

Leigh, Marion, *Findhorn Flower Essences,* Forres: Findhorn Press 1997.
Medeiros, Penny, *Hawaiian Tropical Flower Essences,* Hawaii: My Island Publishing 1995.
Pettit, Sabina (Pacific FEs), *Energy Medicine,* Victoria, BC: Pacific Essences 1993.
Rupa, Dr and Shah, Dr Atul (Aum Himalaya Sanjeevini Essences), *Nature Heals Itself,* Bombay: Aum Himalaya Sanjeevini Essences 1997.
Scherer, Cynthia Athina Kemp (Desert Alchemy), *The Alchemy of the Desert,* Tucson: Desert Alchemy Editions 1997.
Unite, Jannet, *South African Flower Essences,* Constantia, SA: South African Flower and Gem Essences 1995.
White, Ian, *Australian Bush Flower Essences,* Forres: Findhorn Press 1993.
White, Ian, *Bush Flower Healing,* Milsons Point, NSW: Bantam 1999.

Energy and Vibrational Medicine

Baggott, Andy, *The Encyclopedia of Energy Healing,* New Alresford: Godsfield 1999.
Brennan, Barbara-Ann, *Hands of Light,* New York: Bantam 1988.
Chappell, Peter, *Emotional Healing with Homeopathy,* Shaftesbury: Element 1994.
Eden, Donna, *Energy Medicine,* London: Piatkus 1998.
Gerber, Dr Richard, MD, *Vibrational Medicine,* Santa Fe: Bear 1988.
Hall, Alan, Water, *Electricity and Health,* Stroud: Hawthorn 1997.
Harvey, Clare G. and Cochrane, Amanda, *Principles of Vibrational Healing,* London: Thorsons 1998.
Ornish, Dr Dean, *Love and Survival – the Scientific Basis of the Healing Power of Intimacy,* New York: HarperCollins 1998.
Page, Dr Christine, *Frontiers of Health,* Saffron Walden: CW Daniel 1992.
Pert, Dr Candace, *Molecules of Emotion,* London: Simon and Schuster 1997
Watkins, Dr Alan, *Mind–Body Medicine, A Clinician's Guide to Psychoneuroimmunology,* Edinburgh: Churchill Livingstone 1997.
Weil, Dr Andrew, *Health and Healing,* Houghton Miffin 1983.

Flower Remedy Suppliers

UK

International Flower Essence Repertoire (Worldwide Selection)
The Living Tree
Milland
Nr. Liphook, Hants GU30 7JS
Tel: 01428 741572
flower@atlas.co.uk
www.floweressence.co.uk

A Nelson & Co (Bach)
Broadheath House
83 Parkside
Wimbledon
London SW19 5LP
Tel: 0208 780 4200, Fax: 0208 780 4200 5871
www.anelson.co.uk

Healing Herbs (Bach)
PO Box 65
Herefordshire HR2 0UW
Tel: 01873 890218, Fax: 01873 890314
healing-herbs@healing-herbs.co.uk
www.healing-herbs.co.uk

Ainsworths Homeopathic Pharmacy
(Bach and South African Essences)
36 New Cavendish Street
London W1M 7LH
Tel: 0207 935 5330, Fax: 0207 486 4313
enquiries@ainsworths.com
www.ainsworths.com

Crystal Herbs
(Many including Bach, Karmic, Angels, Combinations etc)
1D Gilray Road
Diss
Norfolk IP22 4EU
Tel: 01379 642374, Fax: 01379 641980
information@crystalherbs.com

Carly Gray (Masters)
Low House
Timble, Otley
W Yorks LS21 2NN
Tel and Fax: 01943 880610
cgtimtam@aol.com

Findhorn Flower Essences (Findhorn and Australian Bush)
Wellspring 31 The Park, Findhorn Bay
Findhorn, Forres, Moray
Scotland IV36 3TY
Tel: 01309 690129, Fax: 01309 690933
m4@findhornessences.com
www.findhornessences.com

Sun Essences (Bach and English)
PO Box 728
Norwich NR6 6EX
Tel: 07000 785337, Fax: 01603 712034
sunessence@aol.com
www.sun-essences.co.uk

Bailey Flower Essences Ltd (own)
7/8 Nelson Road, Ilkley
W Yorks LS29 8HN
Tel: 01943 432012, Fax: 01943 432011
baileyfe@aol.com
www.flowervr.com/bailey.html

Harebell Remedies (own)
PO Box 7536
Dumfries
Scotland DG2 7DQ
Tel and Fax: 01387 261962
ellie.web@virgin.net

Silvercord Essences (own)
Turnpike Cottage, Chawleigh
Chulmleigh
Devon EX18 7EU
Tel: 01769 580913
silvercordessences@compuserve.com
www.silvercord-essences.co.uk

Green Man Tree Essences (own)
2 Kerswell Cottages
Exminster, Exeter
Devon EX6 8AY
Tel: 01392 832005
info@greenmantrees.demon.co.uk
www.greenmantrees.demon.co.uk

Phoenix Apothecary (wide range available)
The Park, Findhorn Bay
Forres, Moray
Scotland IV36 3TZ
Tel: 01309 691044, Fax: 01309 690933
phoenix@findhorn.org
www.phoenix-stores.co.uk

Evolution – Stockist of British Flower Essences
117 Fore Street
Exeter Devon EX4 3JQ
Tel and Fax: 01392 410759

Living Light Essences – Janet Warne
14 Lower Abbotsgate
Via Carnforth
Lancashire LA6 2JU
Tel: 015242 72175
www.willtyers.com/livinglight.htm

Europe

Fleurs de Vie – The Flower Essence Company (wide range)
Bôite Postale 2
01170 CHEVRY France
Tel: 04 50 42 62 32, Fax: 04 50 42 62 33
orders@fleursdevie.com
www.fleursdevie.com

DEVA Laboratoire (Phillipe Deroide)
BP9
38880 Autrans
France
www.lab-deva.fr/english/presentation.html

Flower Essences The Netherlands – wide range
Postbus 6139
5960 AC Horst
The Netherlands
Tel: +31-77.39.87.826, Fax: +31-77.39.87.827
Bloesem@Worldonline.nl

Italian Flower Remedies – Spiritual Remedies – wide range
Via Settembrini 1
20124 Milano
Tel: 02 6693950, Fax: 02 6700708

Milagra Flower Essences Ltd – wide range
Saladaviciosa
E-11391 Facinas
Spain
Tel: 34 95 668 7703, Fax: 34 95 668 7828
milagra@retemail.es

Wholefoods Wholesale Ltd – wide range
Unit 2D Kylemore Industrial Estate,
Killeen Road
Dublin 10, Ireland
Tel: 01 626 2315, Fax: 01 626 1233
wholefoods@eircom.net

Chrueter-Drogerie Egger – wide range
Unterstadt 28
8202 Schaffhausen
Switzerland
Tel: 052 624 5030, Fax: 052 624 6457
egger@swissworld.com

Spiren as – wide range
Postboks 2527
7701 Steinkjer
Norway
Tel: 074 167960, Fax: 074 167961

LF Naturprodukte – wide range
Treenering 105
D-24852 Eggebek
Germany
Tel: +49 4609 9102-0, Fax: +49 4609 9102-34
www.lfnatur.com/english/e_index.html

Korte PHI Essenzen
Haupstrasse 9
78267 Aach
Germany
Tel: 07774 7004, Fax: 07774 7009
info@cydon.com

North America

Hawaian Aloha Flower Essences – Penny Medeiros
PO Box 2319
Kealakehua, Hawaii 96750 USA
Tel: 808 328 2529, Fax: 808 328 2529
penalo@qte.com
www.hitrade.com/F.Ess_HmPg.html

FES – Richard Katz and Patricia Kaminski
PO Box 459
Nevada City, CA 95959
Tel: 530 265 9163, Fax: 530 265 0584
mail@flowersociety.org
www.flowersociety.org

Alaskan Flower Essence Project – Steve Johnson
PO Box 1369
Homer, AK 99603 USA
Tel: 907 235 2188, Fax: 907 235 277
info@alaskanessences.com
www.alaskanessences.com

Pacific Essences – Sabina Pettit
PO Box 8317
Victoria, BC V8W 3R9 Canada
Tel: 250 384 5560, Fax: 250 595 7700
Sabina@pacificessences.com
www.pacificessences.com or www.energymedicine.bc.ca

Perelandra – Machaelle Small Wright
PO Box 3603
Warrenton, VA 20188
Tel: 800 960 8806 (US & Canada) or 540 937 2153, Fax: 540 937 3360
www.perelandra-ltd.com

Master's – Lila Devi
14618 Tyler Foote Road
Nevada City, CA 95959
Tel: 800 347 3639 (US & Canada) or 530 478 7655,
Fax: 530 478 7652
mfe@masteressences.com
www.mastersessences.com

Desert Alchemy – Cynthia Athena Kemp Scherer
PO Box 44189
Tucson, AZ 85733
Tel: 800 736 3382 (US & Canada) or 520 325 1545, Fax: 520 325 8405
info@desert-alchemy.com
www.desert-alchemy.com

Petite Fleur – Judy Griffin
8524 Whispering Creek Trail
Fort Worth, Texas 76134
Tel: 817 293 5410, Fax: 817 293 3213
petitefl@flash.net
www.positivehealth.com

Living Light Essences – Jeff Binder
31-130 Cedar Street Suite 424
Cambridge, Ontario, Canada N1S 5A5
Tel: 888 349 3553 (US & Canada) or 519 669 4459, Fax: 519 669 7628
info@livinglightenergies.com
www.livinglightenergies.com

Star Flower Essences
130 W. Figueroa
Santa Barbara, CA 93101
Tel: 805 962 7827, Fax: 805 965 1619
bliss@starfloweressencees.com
www.starfloweressence.com

Cathy Kinnaird – Flower Essence Pharmacy – huge range
PO Box 1147
Sandy, Oregon 97055
Tel: 503 668 7160, Fax: 503 826 1408
info@floweressences.com
www.floweressences.com

Australia and New Zealand

Australian Bush Flower Essences – Ian White
45 Booralie Road
Terrey Hills, NSW 2084 Australia
Tel: 612 9450 1388, Fax: 612 9450 2866
info@ausflowers.com.au
www.ausflowers.com.au

Australian Living Essences – Vasudeva and Kadambii Barnao
Australasian Flower Essence Academy
PO Box 355 Scarborough, WA 6019
Tel: 61 8 9443 5600, Fax: 61 8 9443 5610
email@livingessences.com.au
www.livingessences.com.au

Essences by Sabian – Judi Harvey
55 Studley Park Road or PO Box 527
Kew, Melbourne VIC 3101 Australia
Tel: 61 3 9852 8033, Fax: 61 3 9818 7433
sabian@netspace.net.au

Australian Shell Essences – Leoni Hosey
PO Box 984 Sutherland, NSW 1499 Australia
Tel: 61 2 9528 4106, Fax: 61 2 9584 1803
office@shellessences.com.au

Himalayan Flower Enhancers – Tanmaya
PO Box 43, Central Tilba, NSW 2546
Tel and Fax: 61 2 4473 7131
tanmaya@acr.net.au
www.himalaya.com.au

NZ New Perception Flower Essences
PO Box 60 127
Titirangi
Auckland 1230 New Zealand
Tel and Fax: 64 9 817 7775

Nature's Energy – suppliers
105 Glebe Point Road
Glebe NSW 2037 Australia
Tel: 02 9960 8342, Fax: 02 9960 5584
www.naturesenergy.com.au

Martin and Pleasance – suppliers
137 Swan Street
Richmond, Victoria 3121 Australia
Tel: 02 3 9427 7422

South Africa

South African Flower Essences – Jannet Unite
PO Box 721
Constantia, Cape 7848 South Africa
Tel: 27 21 794 6762 Fax: 27 21 794 7238
info@safloweressences.co.za
www.safloweressences.co.za

India

Aum Himalaya Sanjeevini Essences – Drs Atul and Rupa Shah
15E Jaybharat Society
3rd Road, Khar (West)
Mumbai, Bombay 400 052 India
Tel: 648 68 19 or 604 75 29, Fax:(00 91 22) 605 09 75
rupaatul@bom3.vsnl.net.in
www.aumhimalaya.com or www.energyhealing.net

Brazil

Filhas de Gaia – Maria Grillo
filhadgaia@amhanet.com.br

Araretama Rain Forest Essences – Sandra Epstein
Rua Guararapes 434 apt. 94
Brooklin, Sao Paulo CEP 04561000 Brazil
Tel and Fax: 11 531 9068
araretama@uol.com.br

Saguaro Import – Gustavo and Magdalena Boog – wide range
R Dr Joviano Telles 66, Brooklin, Sao Paulo CEP 04623 120 Brazil
Fax: (55) 11 5561 5096
boog@sti.com.br

Amazonian Orchids – Andreas Korte – see Korte PHI in Europe section

Japan

Heart Support System
801, Okusawa Centre Mansion, 3-47-8
Okusawa
Setagaya-Ku Japan 158
Tel: 03 549 97697, Fax: 03 549 97699

Masanobu Ogawa – author of Flower Essences of the World in Japanese
Tel: 03 5447 7477, Fax: 03 5447 7476
m-ogawa@mars.dti.ne.jp
www.mars.dti.ne.jp/~m-ogawa/index.htm

To find a Practitioner, or Courses

Different makers and various countries have set up their own
professional bodies.
Ask any of the above distributors or makers if you wish to use
a particular range only.

UK resources include

British Flower and Vibrational Essence Association (BFVEA)
8 Willow Glen
Branton
Doncaster DN3 3JD
bfvea@netscapeonline.co.uk
www.members.netscapeonline.co.uk/bfvea/

The Dr Edward Bach Centre
Mount Vernon
Bakers Lane
Sotwell
Oxon OX10 0PZ
Tel: 01491 834678, Fax: 01491 825022
www.bachcentre.com

International Federation of Vibrational Medicine
Middle Picadilly Healing Centre
Holwell, Sherborne
Dorset DT9 5LU
Tel: 01963 23038
ifvm@talk21.com

US resources include

International Academy of Federation of Vibrational Medicine
PMB 654
15600 NE 8th St. B1
Bellevue, WA 98008 USA
Tel: 425 785 3468
info@vibrationalmedicine.com
www.vibrationalmedicine.com

Dr Andrew Tresidder's website

www.dr-andrew-flowers.co.uk

Appendix 1
A Range of Essences

There are now many ranges of essences available from all around the world. Some have particular slants, depending partly on the interest and knowledge of the producer and partly on serendipity. Some of the more well known are briefly described here.

The **Bailey Flower Essences**, made in UK, particularly Yorkshire, are a set that deal with issues of personality and attitudes of mind. They are concerned with coming up to date rather than being held back by past difficulties.

Harebell Essences are made in UK by Ellie Web. They cover a wide range of British wild flowers and relevant aspects of emotion and personality.

South African Flower Essences come from the Cape of Good Hope and surrounding area. Made by Jannet Unite Penny, they deal with deep emotional and spiritual issues.

The **Amazonian Orchid Essences** are made by Andreas Korte, and are powerful enablers of spiritual talents.

Crystal Herbs in the UK make over 400 essences. Prominent among their range are the Angel and Karmic sets, which are again powerful enablers of spiritual talents, and openers of gateways.

Findhorn Fower Essences are made in Scotland by Marion Leigh.

FES from California make the Quintessential set, a second level set that deals with deeper issues of humanity than the Bach. Patricia Kaminski's book *Flowers That Heal* is well worth reading.

Australian Living Essences from near Perth. Some are used in Western Australian hospitals; the Flower Essence Academy is run by the producers, Vasudeva and Kadambii Barnao.

Pacific Essences hail from British Columbia, Canada and include both Flower and Sea essences. They are made by Sabina Pettit.

Desert Alchemy Essences come from the Arizona Desert, and are created by Cynthia Kemp. Cynthia has formulated many important combination essences including Angelic Awareness, Plants and Planets, Celebration of Womanhood and Composite Formula sets.

The Perelandra Essences are a well established range made by Machaelle Small Wright in Virginia USA.

Petite Fleur essences, made by Judy Griffin, come from Texas. Their distinctive feature is that they are not at stock strength, but are mother tincture, in petite bottles.

Aloha Essences come from Hawaii. They are produced by Penny Medeiros, and deal with deeper aspects of spirituality including astral contamination.

Star Essences, based in California, are for the most part made in Peru and South America. Their range includes a useful space freshening 'Crystal Clear' spray.

Alaskan Flower Essences are produced by Steve Johnson from flowers in the tundra of Alaska.

Australian Shell Essences are made in Australia by Leonie Hosie and Nancy Efraemson. Made from shells, not flowers, they too carry a vibrational imprint that has healing powers for humans.

The **Australian Tree Essences** are a set produced by Judi Harvey, and include both waxing and waning essences for each tree, made according to the related moon phase.

New Perception Flower Essences are a set of native New Zealand Essences, made by the Garbelys. Mary has now sadly died.

Aum Himalaya Sanjeevini Essences are made in India by Drs Rupah and Atul Shah, and comprise a large range including disease specific combinations. Himalayan Flower Enhancers are created by Tanmaya.

From Brazil come the **Araratema Rainforest Essences**, made by Sandra Epstein.

Filhas de Gaia is another Brazilian range, created by Maria Grillo.

Bloesem Essences are produced in the Netherlands by Bram Zaalberg.

Deva Laboratories in Southern France produce important ranges, including everyday combinations. Philippe Deroide is the producer.

From Ireland hail the **Ogham Essences** of Róisín Carroll.

Living Light Essences are a set that deal with deep issues of spirituality, made in Canada by Jeff Binder.

Green Man Tree Essences are made by Sue and Simon Lilly in Devon, England. Their range includes many tree, flower and light essences.

Sun Essences (Viv Williamson) produce a range of British flower essences.

Many other makers are coming forward. In UK there are now over 40, some with extensive ranges of British flowers, some like Silvercord Essences including essences from afar. Silvercord (Colin and Diana Kingshott) have made essences in Sweden (fungi) and Iceland. Some, for example Ilminster Essences, make just a few key essences. They are no less important than all the other producers.

As every essence can have a wide range of action in the way of catalysing a healing of emotional, mental and spiritual issues, it is impossible to say which sets may or may not be most appropriate for an individual. In the same way, in a library, we would be foolish to limit ourselves to books by only one author, or one publisher, because there is so much other rich material that we would be denying ourselves. However, we may have our favourites! And when first learning, it's as well to start with A B C!

In summary, this book has featured the Bach, Masters and some of the Australian Bush Essences as being essential foundations before moving further into the use of flower essences. This appendix has detailed many of the better established ranges of essences available worldwide. However, expect to see more and more over the coming years, for essences are emotional nutrients, and there are many yet to be developed.

In the future we can one day expect every town and village to have a library of essences for everyone to share!

Appendix 2
Emotional Health Strategy

This Emotional Health Strategy may be freely copied or adapted for individual or corporate use and is offered for guidance only. Please develop the ideas in any way you wish, and please kindly acknowledge the source on copies or adaptations.

1.1 We all feel better when we are feeling well! Trite perhaps, but still very true. The opposite was recently voiced: 'Feeling miserable doesn't half get you down, doesn't it?' Furthermore, you don't have to feel unwell to want to get better.

1.2 Unfortunately, unless we individually happen to be well already, feeling well seems to be a matter of luck. However, emotional health is a state of well-being that can be attained by each of us, using a personal health strategy. In fact, one of the major barriers to emotional well-being is the attitude of 'I'm fine. I don't need any help'. This attitude reflects the denial mechanism that we all use from time to time to help us deal with our own very personal emotional broken glass.

1.3 A pro-active personal and corporate health strategy can dramatically affect the well-being of many people, both in the workplace and in society at large.

2.1 The knowledge, skills and attitudes needed to attain personal emotional well-being are not difficult to learn. Coping skills are already known to all of us, to varying degrees, and new proactive skills are easily learned.

3.1 The workplace generates some stress and distress, whilst more may come from home or elsewhere. Wherever it is generated, however, emotional distress impacts on to every other area of our lives.

3.2 The cost of not dealing pro-actively to resolve pent-up emotional stress is seen widely in life, its after-effects ranging from frustration to anger, to violence, to alcoholic obliteration, to domestic violence and broken homes, and subsequently reflecting in the behaviour of children and partners.

3.3 Recent litigation is beginning to put pressure on employers to be pro-active in providing emotional health strategies. These may include re-organisation of the workplace to promote greater harmony, and the provision of stress management workshops, performance appraisal techniques and counselling services. Good working practices are already widespread, and need only to be enhanced to cover the emotional component.

3.4 Modern understanding of emotional health has reached the point where it is worth agreeing and implementing an emotional health strategy to involve the whole workforce, not just to deal reactively with problems as they manifest, but to help individuals to enhance their health and well-being. 'You don't have to feel unwell to want to get better.'

3.5 This will necessarily include good communication, good management, and the teaching of personal emotional healing skills that we all can use when alone. Other facilities that may be used include counselling to deal with old or hidden issues, reflexology, aromatherapy, massage, homoeopathy and flower essence therapy – the latter two particularly powerful tools in enhancing health and well-being. The powerful technique of Emotional Stress Release is also a vital skill for us all to master and use personally.

4.1 An emotional health strategy: can we afford not to have one – either at work or for home life? The tragic results of non-action are the partners who are ignored or abused, the children who are shouted at, the emptiness that many feel in their lives, and the collapse into alcoholic- or TV-induced obliteration that so many use – in addition to poor productivity, low morale, and sickness absence. The positive potential is a society comprised of people with profound inner security and self-worth. They tend to say 'How can I help?', 'I can' and 'Why shouldn't I?', rather than 'Can't', 'Shan't' or 'Why should I?' negatives that we so often hear. A challenge for us all to rise to!